Character

The Relationship of

Acupuncture and Psychology

Yves Requena, MD

Paradigm Publications   *Brookline, Massachusetts*

1989

Character and Health by Yves Requena, M.D.

French Edition
Acupuncture et Psychologie
Copyright © 1982 Maloine S.A. Editeur
ISBN 2-224-00862-7

English Edition
Character and Health
Copyright © 1989 Paradigm Publications
ISBN 0-912111-23-2

Library of Congress Cataloging-in-Publication Data

Requena, Yves.
          [Acupuncture et psychologie. English]
          Character and health / Yves Requena.
             p. cm.
          Translation of: Acupuncture et psychologie.
          Bibliography: p.
          Includes index.
          ISBM 0-912111-23-2 : $16.95
          1. Health. 2. Mind and body. 3. Medicine, Chinese I. Title.
RA776.9.R4413 1989
610'.1'9--dc19   819 CIP

Copyright © 1989 Paradigm Publications
44 Linden Street
Brookline, Massachusetts 02146 U.S.A.

Translated by: **Hobart Bell & Associates**

Hobart and Carol Bell

Published by: **Paradigm Publications**

Publisher: Robert L. Felt
Editor: Martha Fielding
Illustrator: Laura Joyce Shaw
Distribution: Redwing Book Company

Foreword

Have you ever wondered if there is a connection between your health and your moods, your health and your lifestyle, your health and your behavior? According to Chinese medicine, there is! Your character — behavioral and psychological tendencies, preferences, dislikes, habits — can predispose you to illness. Knowledge of your character can lead you toward a healthier and happier life.

If you would like to discover what the ancient Chinese knew about your life and health, the information presented in this book, and the tests in chapter 5, will guide you on your voyage of discovery. A simple analysis of the form and structure of your hand, a review of your childhood symptoms, and a scientifically verified character survey, combine to form a finely detailed picture of your character.

Combine what you learn with your own knowledge of your medical history and your family background, and you will know the strengths and weaknesses of your "terrain." With this knowledge you may select the information of greatest benefit to you for individualizing your self-care program.

The material presented is the synthesis of three distinct, yet complementary, medical systems. The first system is the six energies and five constitutions derived from the theories of Chinese acupuncture; the second, the psychological studies of Gaston Berger and his predecessors; the third, the system of trace element therapy, or diathetic medicine, developed in France by Jacques Menetrier. Through his research and study Dr. Requena presents an exciting means of analysis that rewards the reader with useful knowledge that is easily applied.

Any attempt to relate the principles of acupuncture, an ancient Chinese medicine, and psychology, a modern Western somatic medicine, may seem far-fetched at first. Yet, those who pursue the study of acupuncture have come to realize how great is the scope of its compass. Acupuncture is simultaneously a basic and a highly differentiated model of psychosomatic expression. As you will learn, it is a model that includes concepts of constitutions and temperaments not unlike the psychosomatic models proposed by Hippocrates, who inspired the modern theories of biotypology and characterology.

Yet, this book is no mere expression of theory. Its roots are deeply supported by the achievements of ancient Chinese and modern Western science. It addresses fundamental emotions in a manner similar to that of contemporary behaviorists, and it addresses health with the wholistic perspective for which Oriental thought is justly famous. Of the many attempts to express the amazement that is the result of serious study of the Oriental medical tradition, Dr. Requena's most aptly reaches into our lives.

"It is probably true that, in general, the most fertile developments in the history of human thought are born at the intersection of two currents of ideas. These currents may originate in the midst of totally different cultural conditions, in diverse epochs and places. But from the time that they effectively meet and maintain a relationship sufficient for a real interaction to take place, one can hope for new and interesting developments to occur."

> — *Werner Heisenberg*

Introduction to the English Edition

The literature of complementary medicine and self care is extensive. Information regarding diet, herbs, food supplements, and traditional and modern products for health improvement, has become large and widely available. Numerous books detail how yoga, meditation, massage, martial arts, and even Western sports can enhance life and longevity. These are non-invasive practices that may be safely employed with a minimum of concern, if the extreme or excessive are avoided. Complementary therapies, reasonably followed with occasional professional guidance, honor the first rule of all medicine: first, do no harm.

Increasing numbers of physicians recognize the value of complementary therapies. Yet patients and physicians often have no means of effectively speaking to one another. Often, physicians are justly hesitant to endorse programs that are little known in the West, or lack a clinical history. What is lacking is a useful, consistent, and safe method for directing and prioritizing a self-directed program of health maintenance.

Character and Health was written with the intention of providing the understanding and the tools necessary to fill this need. It is a translation, extension and revision of the French work,

Acupuncture et Psychologie (Acupuncture and Psychology). It includes new material and a reorganization of format meant to provide the reader with a coordinated body of information relative to different but complementary aspects of medicine and health. The general reader who is willing to invest a modicum of preparation and study will gain an understanding of his or her own constitution, and hence a means with which to individualize and prioritize a personal program of health care.

Using your terrain as a guide, you can understand your predisposition to disease, and take appropriate action, on your own, and in partnership with your physician. Chapter 8, "Relevance for the Individual" presents direct and comprehensible counsel for the laymen. Chapter 9, "Relevance for the Acupuncturist" discusses terrain for these professionals. Chapter 10, "Relevance for the Psychologist," details some of the statistical support and literature related to the system. Chapter 11, "Relevance for the Physician," presents an overview of scientific issues of interest to the research community.

Table of Contents

Chapter 1

Acupuncture as Medicine

The Therapeutic Range of Acupuncture

"Acupuncture" is actually an interpretive translation of the Chinese ideogram for "needles and fire." It refers to an ancient form of Chinese medicine that involves the insertion of needles into special points on the body located on imaginary lines called meridians. The needles may be replaced by, or used with, moxibustion or moxa burning, a technique where heat is applied to the acupuncture points.

Documentation of the efficacy of these treatments is increasing as a result of research and application by major medical universities. Acupuncture is widely acknowledged in the West as a means of surgical anesthesia, and as a treatment for specific pains such as neuralgia and rheumatism. Moxibustion also has been verified to be of benefit in the treatment of chronic rheumatism, anemia, and certain degenerative diseases.[1]

Acupuncture treatments given over a period of several sessions typically result in a gradual alleviation and cessation of the patient's discomfort. The mechanism underlying this relief is not merely symptomatic, but acts on the disease process itself. For example, a person suffering from arthrosis of the knee does not experience immediate relief after a single session of acupuncture

1

therapy. Several sessions are required for the relief of pain to occur, as well as for the liberation of articular stiffness. With successive treatments, however, the mobility of the joint gradually increases, a mobility that appears to oppose the underlying degenerative process.[2] Acupuncture therapy may thus be seen as a means of reversing the disease process. To confine the application of acupuncture to the alleviation of pain would unfairly limit the scope of its therapeutic potential. The effect of acupuncture therapy involves a reequilibration of the basic energetic functioning of the body, and as such can have profound effects on illness and health.

The application of acupuncture techniques is also beneficial in the treatment of certain psychological disorders, such as insomnia.[3] Alcohol, tobacco, and drug dependence is another arena of medical care where the application of acupuncture therapy demonstrates dramatic results.[4]

In the same way that doubts remain among certain medical practitioners concerning the effectiveness of acupuncture for viral infections and visceral afflictions, its effectiveness in treating mental states is viewed with reserve. It is difficult for a practitioner with little background in the study of acupuncture medicine to imagine how, with needles inserted into the skin, one can soothe anguish, ameliorate depression, or relieve insomnia. It has even been said that acupuncture is a simple act of autosuggestion. Yet why would autosuggestion play a role only with acupuncture treatments and not with Western medicaments?

To understand acupuncture and comprehend how it can work at the same time for the body and for the mind, it is helpful to have a precise idea of the general theories and precepts. Setting aside any preconceived notions that we may have regarding acupuncture, let us begin by viewing it as an electric model of the human body.

The Electric Model

The ancient Chinese discovered that the skin is covered with acupuncture points, themselves situated on meridians that are imaginary lines or channels. Energy, in the form of a bioelectric current, was found to circulate along these specific channels, the meridians. Though they did not define the energy in a "scientific" fashion, they did describe it as a flux polarized in yin and yang, negative and positive. This occurrence, suggesting an electric current, is possible to verify by holding a neutral electrode in one hand, while a charged electrode is applied to an acupuncture point, a specific site on the skin along a meridian. A microcurrent passed through the electrode creates a difference in electrical potential. A small amplifier connected to a branch circuit will make the electric signal audible.

In all, there are 133 meridians: 12 principal meridians, 8 extraordinary meridians, and others such as the channel sinews, channel divergences, and connecting vessels. On the surface of the body each principal meridian communicates with both the preceding meridian and the following one in an unending loop of the 12 meridians. On each of these networks there exist principal and secondary points, as well as principal and secondary points that connect each of these networks to the others. In short, each of the 12 meridians, besides the internal course that links the meridian to its organ, possesses 4 secondary meridians that establish relationships with bone, tendon and muscle, with the interior and the other viscera, as well as with those meridians in close proximity. In this it is rather like the collateral channels and capillaries between the arteries and veins.

Just as the heart serves as the physical pump of the arteriovenous system, the lung serves as the pump for the energetic system. Thanks to the dynamics of respiration, the energy of this circuit is in continual circulation. It is principally because of these dynamics that the acupuncturist sees the meridians and their interrelationships as responsive and mobile rather than uniform and static. To view the meridians as devoid of such dynamism is a serious error, something akin to observing a photograph of the large arteries without seeing either the movement of the blood or its rate. Illustrations of acupuncture meridians and points convey nothing of the real dynamism that exists within the system.

The bioelectric model permits us to see that a flux of energy circulates, and that this flux is comparable to a natural electromagnetism. It is electric in the sense that it can be registered and measured at the acupuncture points, and it is most likely magnetic as well. At the moment such a description is only hypothetical.[5] An upper and lower polarity of the body also exists, described thus in Chinese texts: "Man is between the sky and the earth; the sky is yang, the earth is yin. Likewise the top of the body, the head, is yang, the lowest part, the feet, is yin."

Polarization also is reflected in the left and right halves of the body, the left being yang and the right yin, as well as in the back and front of the body, the back being yang and the front yin.

To illustrate by analogy the function of this electronic system, one can compare the physiology of the body to a transistor radio. The organs can be viewed as the station detectors, the volume and tonality controls, the selectors of short, medium or long wavelengths, the semiconductors and the amplifier. All organs are linked by a complex network of wires, transistors, condensers, and resistors. Let us say for ease of comparison that all the electric circuits are on the surface of the apparatus and spread over all its faces. When the radio is in good operating condition, that is, when the antennae are properly oriented, the reception is normal and the proper conversion of signals occurs; transmission is perfect. This state is analogous to the body in good health. If, however, a problem occurs in any of the circuits, the unit as a whole is disturbed. Function is no longer harmonious; there is, as it were, a functional illness. For service, a technician is called.

The action taken by an electronics technician in repairing the circuitry of a radio is analogous to that taken by the acupuncturist when pricking certain points in the acupuncture network of the body. Having examined the system and determined, through an analysis of the symptoms, the source of the disruption, action is taken to tonify or disperse, accelerate or decelerate, unblock or divert the energy in those parts of the meridian system where the energy flow has been disrupted.[6]

When a breakdown is not repaired in time, the circuit continues to suffer and the organs remain in disharmony. This disharmony ultimately results in a real breakdown, creating an irreversible alteration of the organ. In Western medicine this is the state called organic illness.

4

The Cosmic Model

The ancient Chinese conceptualization of humanity, nature, and illnesses is not as simplistic as it may appear at first sight. The Chinese view of human physiology is based on a concept of energy fields, a view comparable to the modern concept of an energetic field that has arisen in contemporary physics (8). According to this idea, space and matter are inseparable. Matter is viewed as being constituted of regions in space where the field is extremely intense. The field represents the sole reality.

The influence of Taoist philosophy has doubtless contributed to the elaboration of this model, for, in Taoism, it is held that the material world rises out of an "initial emptiness" or a "great void." This description also brings to mind the concept of a physical void underlying modern field theory. The void spoken of by the Chinese is composed of qi, a term difficult to translate but perhaps adequately rendered by the word "breath" or "energy." According to an explanation offered by the philosopher Tchang Tsai, "The qi has but to condense to form all things, and these things have only to be dispersed to form once again the great void." (9)

This ancient point of view is similar to that of contemporary scholars. As is the universe, the Taoists felt, so is humankind. We are made up of matter, thus of void and of qi, which bring form and substance. As a form, man represents a specific field that is distinct from the rest of the universe. The qi flows through this field within the network of meridians. During circulation the qi gives rise to the primary metabolisms. As we are a part of the void, however, we are linked to the integral field of the universe, and our relationships with the environment and with the rest of the world are thus inseparable.

This concept of Taoist philosophy is reminiscent of the modern notion of synchronicity. The astrophysicist Hoyle writes:

> Recent developments in cosmology have come to suggest that everyday situations do not go on independent of the far reaches of the universe, and all our ideas of

5

space and geometry would be totally invalidated if
these far reaches were excluded. Our everyday experience, to the tiniest detail, seems to be so closely linked
to the scale of the universe that it is nearly impossible
to consider that the two exist separately (8).

This inseparability is what the ancient Chinese held to be true
in physiology. It was of course impossible at that time to attempt
a more specific approach, but the Chinese intuitively perceived
the similarity between the structure of humans and that of the
universe. With the spirit of analogy that is inherent in their way
of thinking, they related the warp and weave of the universe to
the smallest of objects. The Taoist concept of intimate bonds and
synchronicity between all objects in the universe, and particularly
of humankind with the rest of the cosmos, was without doubt at
the origin of their cosmological approach to physiology.

In acupuncture this approach is elaborated in what we call the
precursor model, and is described in contemporary terms as
modern chronobiology. Humanity depends on the environment
for biological rhythms. We submit and must adapt to climatic
conditions, the lunar rhythm, the rhythm of the seasons and various heavenly influences.

Climatic Conditions

Chinese medicine recognizes five different climatic conditions:
coldness and heat, humidity and dryness, and wind. These five
climatic conditions act on the meridial network system of the
body and, through these networks, on the bodily functions.
These meridial networks are vulnerable to climatic conditions
according to the particular affinities of the meridians and their
respective organs. For example, the heart meridian and the heart
are sensitive to heat, are more vulnerable at midday and in the
heat of summer, to the sun at its solstice, etc. The meridians of
the liver and gallbladder are sensitive to wind. The functions of
the kidney and bladder meridians are disequilibrated by the cold,
and during this time persons suffering from this perturbation feel,
as but one example, an imperative need to urinate.

The Circadian Rhythm

The rhythm of day and night, the circadian rhythm, is manifested in the circulation of the energy in the meridians. One meridian and its respective functions are hyperactive at each hour of the Chinese day. (One hour in Chinese medicine is equal to two hours in the West. A day, therefore, is equal to 12 rather than 24 hours.)

The Chinese Clock	
Meridian	*Time*
Lung	3:00 a.m. to 5:00 a.m.
Large Intestine	5:00 a.m. to 7:00 a.m.
Stomach	7:00 a.m. to 9:00 a.m.
Spleen	9:00 a.m. to 11:00 a.m.
Heart	11:00 a.m. to 1:00 p.m.
Small Intestine	1:00 p.m. to 3:00 p.m.
Bladder	3:00 p.m. to 5:00 p.m.
Kidney	5:00 p.m. to 7:00 p.m.
Pericardium	7:00 p.m. to 9:00 p.m.
Triple Burner	9:00 p.m. to 11:00 p.m.
Gallbladder	11:00 p.m. to 1:00 a.m.
Liver	1:00 a.m. to 3:00 a.m.

At its hour of activity the meridian is a full reservoir of energy, functioning at maximal level. The first meridian, that of the gallbladder, corresponds to the first Chinese hour, from 11 p.m. to 1 a.m.

Many empirical observations confirm a correspondence to the Chinese concept of biological rhythm. For example, persons suffering from hepatic distress, i.e., from gallbladder sensitivity, are insomniacs — or at least prefer to go to bed late. The time of the lung meridian coincides with the frequency of nocturnal attacks observed in asthmatics. The meridian of the large intestine is most active in the hours from 5 a.m. to 7 a.m., the period most frequently associated with bowel movement. Passage of stools at this time is easier than in the evening, because the colon is at a level of maximal activity. The stomach meridian hour, 7 a.m. to 9 a.m., is considered the most favorable for digestion; many dieticians advise their patients to eat a large breakfast. This advice follows all the more logically because the meridian of the spleen and pancreas, organs vital to digestive process, are at maximal activity in the following hour, from 9 a.m. to 11 a.m. Persons who have breakfasted insufficiently find that they are most drained during this period. The lowered level of sugar metabolism cannot be properly regulated by the pancreas.

Recognition of these observable rhythms and their relationship to physiologic function is essential to acupuncture therapy. In serious or chronic illnesses it serves the practitioner to utilize the hours of maximal activity of the organ for correcting any disequilibrium.[7]

The Lunar Rhythm

According to Chinese medicine the moon exerts an influence on the body fluids similar to the influence it exerts on the ocean tide. In acupuncture theory, this fluid tide is the play of equilibrium between two forces, the dynamism of the blood circulation, arterial and venous, and the global energy of the meridians. These forces work simultaneously in the organism in a balance both complementary and opposed. In the *Nei Jing*, the classic ancient text on acupuncture, this is noted emphatically:

> At the new moon the blood and the energy begin to be purified. At the full moon, the blood and energy are in abundance. During the wane of the moon the muscles relax, the meridians and extraordinary vessels empty themselves, the container no longer adapts to its contents. The occurrence of these bodily changes is why the ordering of the blood and energy by the techniques of acupuncture must include the study of celestial phenomena and their influence on the body. The acupuncturist thus should not disperse at the new moon, tonify at the full moon, or puncture at the waning of the moon.

In this regard it is interesting that modern statistical findings aptly corroborate the observations of the ancient Chinese doctors. In a study led by a U.S. surgeon, post-operative hemorrhages were found to be more frequent during periods of the full moon (37).

The Seasonal Rhythm

The rhythm of the seasons also influences the meridians and organs. The liver is at maximum activity in the spring; the heart in summer; following August 15 (considered the fifth season), the spleen-pancreas; the lung in autumn; and the kidney in winter.

This variation in the activity of the organs can be observed clinically by feeling the Chinese pulses in the wrist. If, for example, in the area where one usually palpates for the liver pulse, the pulse is barely perceptible, whereas the other areas are more palpable, and it is springtime, the acupuncturist can diagnose in this patient an insufficiency of the liver. In general, such a condition may manifest as pollen allergies, hay fever, sneezing, and conjunctivitis, and the sensation of an irritant in the eyes.

Heavenly Influences

According to Chinese medicine and astronomy, there exist no less than 108 stars, planets, or constellations that can influence an organism. These celestial bodies, other than the sun and moon, were grouped according to mathematical calculation and then simplified and organized as the influence of five essential planets: Jupiter, Mars, Saturn, Venus, and Mercury. Since the beginning of acupuncture these influences were so well studied and were considered so dramatic that they were incorporated into the general theories of Chinese physiology. They are an integral part of the climatic, seasonal, circadian, annual, monthly, and hourly chronobiological phenomena.

In terms of a contemporary understanding of any heavenly influence, the current practice of astronomy does not establish any scientific, measurable physical influence from these celestial bodies, nor seek to determine a precise nature for it, except for the existence of magnetic radiation from those planets close to the earth. This absence of detailed information is both a function of emphasis (Western medicine is not interested in such influences and simply denies their existence in the majority of cases) and measurement difficulty.

The cosmic model of acupuncture complements the electronic model. To visualize all the various movements of energy in the meridians in relation to their cosmic influences, let us imagine that

9

these meridians, on a very small scale, are like canals that gradually but simultaneously swell day after day as the moon waxes, and diminish as the moon wanes. As mentioned previously, the energy progresses through the meridians in a never-ending loop at the speed of approximately 240 cm per minute. One meridian is more energetic than another depending on the hour of the day, the season, the temperature, and the climate. Not only at each hour, but also at each minute, a point related to a particular planet resonates in harmony with it and is "open." That is, it is full of energy, and thus it is a favorable time for the insertion of needles.

To be precise, for each hour there are two points on each side of the body that are open, one point among the 12 principal meridians and one among the eight extraordinary vessels. Each obeys a specific chronology in accordance with the Chinese system of hours. Everything happens as if one were seeing the meridians follow four different movements. The meridians fill and empty in time with the periods of the moon; there is a progressive advance of energy in time with respiration. A selective filling of one meridian over another moves like a wave that, superimposing itself upon respiration, fills the meridians, one after another at different speeds. There is a selective rise of meridians related to the season and climate. Some points are energized and others are extinguished depending on the various influences upon them.

All these climatic, hourly, seasonal, circadian, and astronomical conditions intermingle with one another according to laws the Chinese have precisely defined. It is important to note that these conditions are not, of necessity, harmful sources of perturbation for humans. They may adversely affect the body only if the body physiology is in disequilibrium or vulnerable, i.e., not in perfect health. Thus, to use the analogy described earlier, in the absence of perfect health the body functions rather as the radio set functions without an appropriate antenna or without being well grounded. The cosmic influences disturb the message and thus disrupt the broadcast, very much as a thunderstorm disrupts radiowave emissions.

A further element that contributes to the maintenance of this bodily equilibrium is the psychological state of the individual. Having glimpsed according to acupuncture the physical aspect of the "energy-matter" system that is the human body, and recognizing as well how it is subject to environmental influences, it is necessary to consider the influence of the psychological character on this model.

The Psychosomatic Model

In the most ancient acupuncture texts it is stated that if the mental state is at peace and equilibrated the person is less, indeed not at all, subject to illness, even illness of external origin through the influence of cosmic or climatic energies. He or she will be susceptible to no disease, even infections. This proposition is quite absolute.

In Chinese medicine, behavior is classified according to five primary tendencies. These are tendencies to anger and outbursts of rage, to excessive joy or emotion, to excessive reflection and worry, to sadness and withdrawal, and to fear. In the view of Chinese physicians, each of these tendencies can disorganize the system. The disorganization occurs in a very specific way, acting selectively on a meridian and on an organ. For example, anger in excess harms the meridians of the liver and gallbladder and their respective organs. This disorganization of the meridian leads to other vulnerabilities. For example, in springtime, the seasonal period in which the liver is more active, strong wind is harmful to the liver and engenders various problems.

These behavioral tendencies can be compared to the more recent classification of behavior by the neurophysiologist MacLean (25). He distinguishes six general emotions: desire leading to constant striving, anger leading to aggressivity, fear leading to the need to protect oneself, sadness bringing despondency, joy leading to feelings of gratitude, and affection producing excessive sentimentality.

Chinese medicine goes still further in its consideration of the psychological character of an individual, offering the notion of the "vegetative spirit," *Shen.*

Shen and Jing

Among the 12 physiological functions, five are under the command of the five most important meridians of the body — the heart, liver, spleen-pancreas, lung, and kidney. The organs assigned to these meridians are "full" *(zang)* organs, in contrast to the "hollow" *(fu)* organs such as the intestines, bladder, and gallbladder, considered organs of transit.

In Chinese physiology, each of the five full or solid organs is nourished by blood and energy. Blood is carried by the vessels, energy by the meridian and its internal trajectory. Blood and energy bring whatever ingredients are necessary for the organ to function properly. Each organ thus is able to fulfill its appropriate role: the lung respires, the heart pumps blood, the kidney eliminates waste, etc. In addition to its primary function, each organ elaborates a particular energy, an energy essential, pure, precious. This energy is called jing; it also circulates in the meridians.[8]

Each energy has distinctive physiologically and psychologically active emanations, described in contemporary terms as substances of the central nervous system (CNS). Each substance is also different according to the organ. The substance of the liver is called *hun*, that of the kidney *zhi*, that of the spleen-pancreas *yi*, of the lung *po*, of the heart *shen*. The Chinese term used to designate the entire group of CNS substances is also *Shen*. The capitalization emphasizes the group concept as distinct from the elaboration of jing from the heart organ.

Each CNS substance related to the organ is also linked to psychological behavior. An excess of activity of the liver organ, for example, produces an excess of hun and leads to angry behavior. The inverse is also true. Insufficient activity of the liver brings on an insufficient elaboration of hun, the capacity to act on one's environment, to be aggressive and defend oneself. Such an insufficiency leads to timidity, anxiety, and lack of self-confidence, evidencing the relationship of the health of the organ and the psychological state.

Many chapters in the classic Chinese acupuncture texts are devoted to this relationship between the organs and psychological temperament. One can read in these works that sorrows trouble the energy of the heart meridian and organ, that anger directly troubles the liver meridian and organ, joy makes flexible the functioning of the circulation of energy and broadens the feelings, anger upsets the course of energy in the meridians, sadness tightens the heart and injures the lung meridian and organ, and fear despoils the essential energy, jing, of the whole body. An entire chapter in the *Nei Jing* gives further examples of the relationship of health and the mental state. An excess of worry injures the spleen-pancreas meridian; anger engenders death by stroke; great fear can lead to psychosis; pains act on the liver and are manifested by muscle contractions (frequent attacks of muscular spasms and tetany). This chapter also relates that an absence of energy in the liver produces fear and anxiety; an abundance produces constant anger.

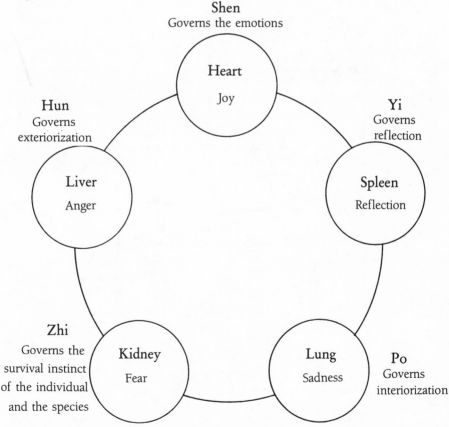

Figure 1: The five shen and the five fundamental emotions and their connection to the brain.

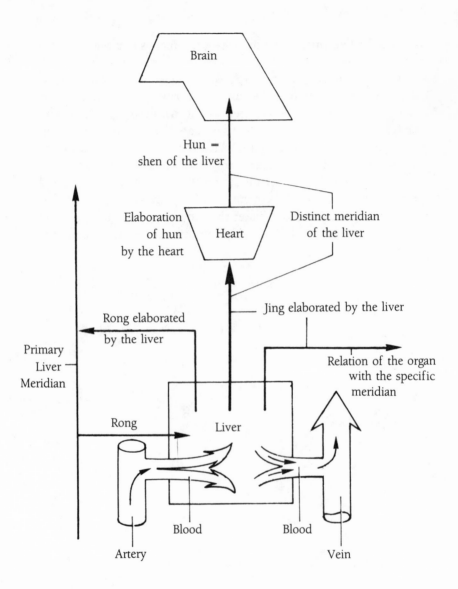

Figure 2: Elaboration of jing by the liver and hun by the heart, and their connection to the brain.

We can summarize the Chinese concepts of psychological behavior by saying that the organs elaborate a particular energy that is carried to the heart meridian by the other meridians. The heart meridian elaborates these shen, then conducts them to the brain. In these ideas we recognize the concept of humor that was popular in Greek medicine, as set forth by Hippocrates (460-370 B.C.). The concept was promulgated later by Galen (130-200 C.E.), who defined four temperaments: choleric (bilious or bad-tempered), sanguine, melancholic, and phlegmatic. Linked to these four temperaments was also a fifth, the quintessential. In acupuncture, however, these emanations were regarded to be more in the immaterial, energetic domain than in the peripheral domain of the body.

If we compare these concepts with the neuroendocrinological concepts of behavior in Occidental medicine, jing would represent the hormonal secretions that are specific to each organ. Thus, because the kidney is linked to the gonad, its jing should correspond to the secretion of testosterone in the testes and pro-gesterone in the ovaries. The Shen, the CNS substances, would thus represent the consequences of the endocrine secretion of the different jing energies on the psychological behavior.

Using this level of correspondence, numerous parallels can be established. An excess of hun in the liver is associated with hyperthyroidism, for which the behavior is characterized by irri-tability and nervous tension, and is accompanied by muscular hyperexcitability. The excess in the liver is also related to hyper-follicular activity, which results in painful swelling of the breasts and painful menstrual periods. However, the claim of a correspondence should not be taken in its literal sense. The jing energy and its emanations, the Shen, are envisaged by the Chinese as immaterial phenomena circulating in an independent fashion through their respective meridians, and not, according to the Western view, as hormones circulating in the blood vessels. Furthermore, in Chinese medical theory, the neuroendocrine rela-tionship does not occur of necessity in the brain, with a large role played by the thalamus, hypothalamus, and pituitary glands, as is the case according to the Western concept of physiology; rather, it is believed to occur in the heart. Thus, when the ancient Chinese physicians spoke of the heart as the place of elaboration of the Shen, it was not the material heart to which they were referring but an organizational center connected to the meridians.

Westerners believe that the body is organized by the brain, and as such, this organ should be regarded as the governor of behavior. The Chinese believe that this capacity is a function of the heart region. Popular tradition conveys much the same idea. Innumerable expressions allude to the heart as an emotive center: "to have a heavy heart," conveying sorrow; "to sing to your heart's content," conveying contentment; "to have a tender heart," conveying compassion. Perhaps the best illustration of the preeminence of the heart over the brain is the maxim, "the heart has its reasons that reason does not know."

The energetic quality of this center, of the same nature as that of the meridians, allows us to explain why a number of important acupuncture points in the cardiac region bear names of psychological import. The points of the heart meridian itself have names such as "route of the spirit" and "doorway of the spirit;" they are important in the therapeutic treatment of psychological problems. Even the Chinese characters for psychology connote this understanding, for the ideograms translate as "reason (principle) of the heart."[9]

Thus we may begin to see that the Chinese view of humanity and our relationship to the universe is synchronistic, whole, as exciting and applicable as our most modern sciences, and is expressed in clear and useful principles.

Chapter 2

The Foundations of Acupuncture

The Principle of Yin-Yang

The yin-yang principle arose from the Chinese relativistic view of the world. It is a view in which all observed phenomena are grouped into two sets. (The term "set" is used here in the same sense it is used in contemporary mathematics — a logically related grouping.) One set is yin, the other yang. The primary symbol of yin is earth, that of yang, the sky. Humanity, which is between the earth and the sky, proceeds from both.

The yin set includes the more material, heavy, and large phenomena, such as solids, the body, excretions; the more inert phenomena, such as rest, immobility, death; and the colder and deeper phenomena, such as cold, ice (dense water), winter, the interior, anything hidden or deep. Also categorized as yin are the night, the moon, the female. The yang set includes the gases, the energy of the meridians, mental activity, physical activity, life, heat, water vapor, summer, the visible (unhidden), the shallow (superficial), day, the sun, the male.

Classification of Yin-Yang	
Yin	Yang
matter	energy
material	electromagnetic
organs	meridians
night	day
moon	sun
female	male
winter	summer
heavy	light
large	small
solids	gas
bodily excretions	psychological expressivity
rest	activity
death	life
immobility	mobility
cold	hot
ice	vapor
interior	exterior
hidden	manifest
deep	superficial

The binary principle of yin and yang is not the result of empirical speculation. It is the result of the inductive, theoretical concepts inherited from the metaphysical and philosophical culture of ancient China where the world was viewed with both a transcendent and immanent sense (17). Taoist philosophy regards yin-yang as a principle of antagonism by which the unique principle of everything, the Tao, is non-material, permanent, and potential rather than kinetic. The Tao can be materialized in the physical world, but the materialization is not permanent.

Yin and yang are never fixed or static. There exists between the two poles an active bond, a complementarity like male and female, a dynamic state of alternation like day and night, a movement between the two, such as an excess of yang being transformed into yin, and vice versa. Yin-yang embraces the alternation between the one and many, between the transcendent and immanent, between instinct and sublimation.

18

This complementarity is applicable to numerous domains in the physical world, and explains well the universal principle of homogeneity and heterogeneity that science has demonstrated in all laws of nature, the principle of entropy and negentropy. It explains the cybernetic organization of physical laws, and particularly those biological laws represented schematically as action-reaction-retroaction.[10] It is a principle active in living matter, even at the cellular level, as Arthur Koestler describes in his work, *The Horse and the Locomotive.*

In climatology, yin-yang is represented by the alternation of the seasons. We see here too the concept of transformation, in which yin becomes yang and vice versa. The process of transformation occurs in transitional stages, and, as shown in the figure, occurs not only for the seasons, but for the day, which includes the poles of noon and midnight.

In this figure one can also see that the four seasons, with their two solstices and two equinoxes, correspond to the four phases of transformation of yin-yang. If we represent them as two levels, there is the yang of the yang phase, corresponding to summer; the yin of the yin phase, corresponding to winter. The yang of yin phase corresponds to spring, which is the passage from winter to summer. There is in this phase an equality of yin and yang, and this is equivalent to the equinoxes, at which time day equals night. The yin of yang phase corresponds to autumn, which is the passage from summer to winter. Yin and yang are equal in this phase as well, and this equality is the autumnal equinox, the time when night equals day. These four phases are superimposable on the Tai Qi symbol (Figure 3, following page).

In medicine, yin and yang are illustrated in antagonistic processes like the interaction of antigens and antibodies, poisons and antidotes, activating and inhibiting substances, acetylcholine and adrenalin, the sympathetic and parasympathetic activity of the autonomic nervous system.[11]

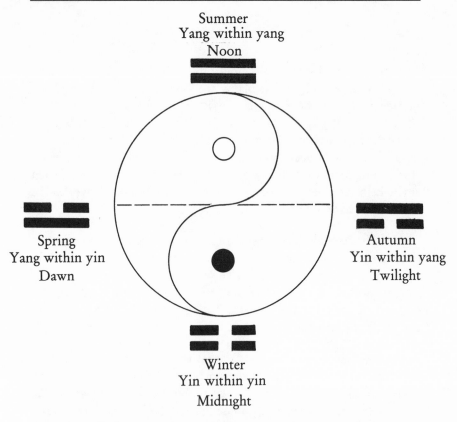

Figure 3: The four seasons and four phases of yin-yang.

Because of the ubiquity of the yin-yang principle in the universe, the ancient Chinese used this principle to classify behavior. In the earliest surviving text on acupuncture, the *Nei Jing (Yellow Emperor's Classic of Internal Medicine)*, the imperial physician explained to his emperor, "Persons with an excess of yang have a high level of spirit and energy; such individuals tend to speak quickly and are highly active." Although a man is considered yang and a woman yin, there exist yin and yang individuals independent of their gender. Likewise it is possible to find yin men (men with yin behavior) and yang women. The polar relationship that exists between hot and cold in physical phenomena is also held to exist in behavior. Thus, it is possible to distinguish persons who are of cold, yin temperament from those of hot, animated, yang temperament. The various aspects and the myriad forms that exist in behavior as a result of the yin-yang principle will be considered in greater detail in later chapters.

The yin-yang principle can be applied to a classification of the viscera as well. The hollow organs *(fu)* are yang. They function in the transit of materials through the body. The *fu* organs and meridians include the small intestine, the bladder, the large intestine, stomach, gallbladder and triple burner. The full or solid organs *(zang)* are yin. These organs behave as a reservoir or storehouse. Metabolism occurs here, as well as the elaboration of the essential jing energy of each organ. The *zang* organs and meridians include the heart, liver, kidney, lung, spleen-pancreas, and the pericardium.

The Six Energies

According to the principle of yin-yang, the twelve principal meridians and their associated twelve functions are classified by twos into six categories that are called the six energies. The categories include a great yang (Tai Yang), a small yang (Shao Yang), a luminous yang (Yang Ming), a great yin (Tai Yin), a small yin (Shao Yin), and a terminal yin (Jue Yin).

The yang meridians emerge and convene (anastomose) on the surface (yang) of the body at the level of the head (yang). The bladder meridian follows the small intestine meridian, the triple burner meridian follows the gallbladder meridian, etc. The meridians listed on the left of the preceding figure run along the arm, and are called *shou* (hand). Those on the right run along the lower leg, and are called *zu* (foot). Thus, the small intestine meridian begins in the head and follows the arm up to the head, where it continues as the bladder meridian. This is the Tai Yang meridian; it passes along the arm and is called *shou tai yang.* The bladder meridian that terminates in the lower leg and foot is called *zu tai yang.* As Tai Yang is the largest and most superficial yang, its network includes the posterior surface (yang), the most external part of the arm and back (more yang than the front of the body), and the thigh and lower leg in a posterior (yang) and exterior (yang) course. Shao Yang follows a similar pathway, though it circulates along the middle, posterior, and external surfaces of the limbs, and along the side of the body. Yang Ming runs on the most internal surface of the yang surfaces of the arms and legs, and on the abdomen, because the abdomen is the least yang of the three. The same reasoning applies to the yin meridians that convene on the interior of the body (yin) and not superficially on the skin.

21

These six meridians, Tai Yang, Shao Yang, Yang Ming, and Tai Yin, Jue Yin, Shao Yin, connect the top and bottom of the body. A meridian of the arm and top part of the body, the lung meridian, for example, *shou tai yin,* is connected to a meridian of the leg and lower part of the body, the spleen-pancreas meridian, *zu tai yin.* The two together constitute a single meridian, Tai Yin.

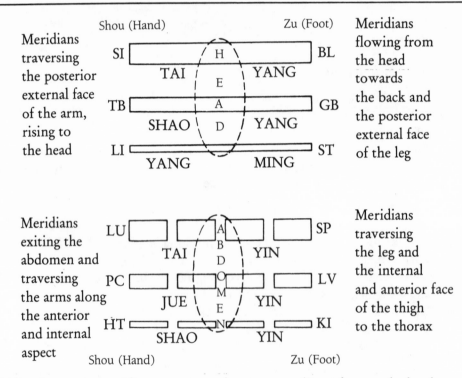

The three yang meridians emerge and convene at the surface on the head. The three yin meridians emerge and convene at the interior in the abdomen.

NB: By convention, the yang meridians are represented by continuous lines, and the yin meridians by broken lines. The width of the line is proportional to the degree of yin or yang.

Figure 4: The six energies or six meridians

The preceding classification of the six meridians is of major importance in the scheme of acupuncture. It explains how a pathologic phenomenon can be propagated from the bottom to the top of the body, or vice versa, and why an acupuncturist will treat a migraine headache by pricking points on the foot. Furthermore, it establishes a connection between organ functions that, in the West, typically are regarded as separate.

Apparently inexplicable observations of associations between disturbances in the lung, spleen, and pancreas are immediately more understandable when these organs are viewed as parts of the Tai Yin meridian. As examples, in mucoviscidosis, a genetic disease of the pancreas, respiratory signs are an important aspect of the disease. Suddenly stopping smoking usually results in excessive eating and weight gain, due not to psychological factors as is commonly supposed, but to poor regulation of sugar metabolism by the pancreas. (Tobacco, a drug acting on the lung, also has the effect of diminishing the appetite.) Western observations often confirm the theory of Chinese physicians who consider whooping cough more an illness of the spleen-pancreas than of the lung.

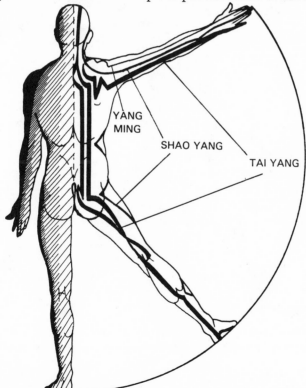

Figure 5A: The yang meridians

The most yang meridians traverse the external posterior part and the most superficial part of the skin, which is yang; the yin meridians traverse the anterior, internal, and deepest part, which is yin. Thus, humans, who are between yang sky and yin earth, are polarized in yin-yang. The meridians follow and even imprint this polarity, like the lines of force surrounding a magnet that align iron filings between the north and south poles (head and feet).

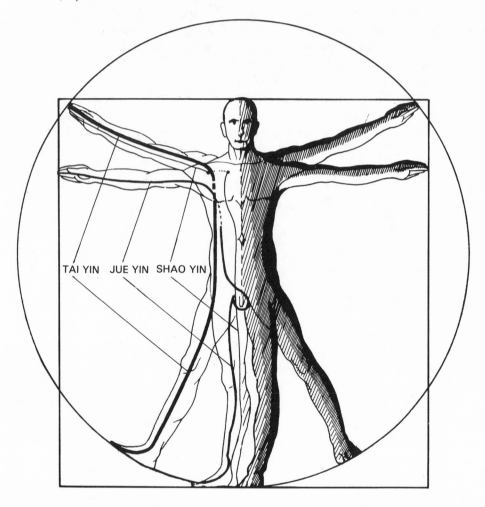

TAI YIN   JUE YIN   SHAO YIN

Figure 5B: The yin meridians

The ancient Chinese also grouped individuals into behavioral types as a function of the six energies and six corresponding paired meridians, giving precise indications about the personality and physiological make-up characteristic of each type. The six meridians defined six types of constitutional association:

Meridian	Element/Meridian Pairs	
Tai Yang	Fire—Small Intestine	Water—Bladder
Shao Yang	Wood—Gallbladder	Fire—Triple Burner
Yang Ming	Earth—Stomach	Metal—Large Intestine
Tai Yin	Earth—Spleen-Pancreas	Metal—Lung
Shao Yin	Water—Kidney	Fire—Heart
Jue Yin	Wood—Liver	Fire—Pericardium

This classification of the twelve meridians into six great meridians or six energies is applicable to environmental conditions as well. The six energies are at the origin of the six distinct climatic conditions: coldness, wind, heat, damp, fire, and dryness. These correspond respectively to the Tai Yang, Jue Yin, Shao Yin, Tai Yin, Shao Yang, and Yang Ming meridians. Each meridian is sensitive and vulnerable to its corresponding climatic condition. A weakness in the liver meridian *(zu jue yin)*, for example, would predispose the liver to vulnerability to the wind.[12]

The Five Elements

Another system of classification based on the yin-yang concept groups observable phenomena into sets of five rather than six. The sets are named by the elements wood, fire, earth, metal, water. While the words are the same, these Chinese terms do not refer to esoteric theories that use primary elements as the foundation of matter, such as in Indian metaphysics. The use of these symbols by the Chinese is quite different from that of the Indians (17).[13] The Chinese five elements, as noted by the sinologist Marcel Granet in his work, *Chinese Thought,* are references to a spatial-temporal classification of phenomena. It goes beyond the idea that spatial and temporal positions exist separately, which is the belief generally held by ancient Greek and, later, Western thinkers.

The Chinese view of the five elements places each element along the circumference of a circle. The classification is regarded by the Chinese as universally valid. It, as it were, decodes the universe, by placing each of its elements into coherent sets. A given element corresponds to a period of the daily cycle, a climate (via the same logical relation as with the six energies), a planet (one submitting to the influence of another), a color, an animal, a metal, a tone of the Chinese musical scale, etc.

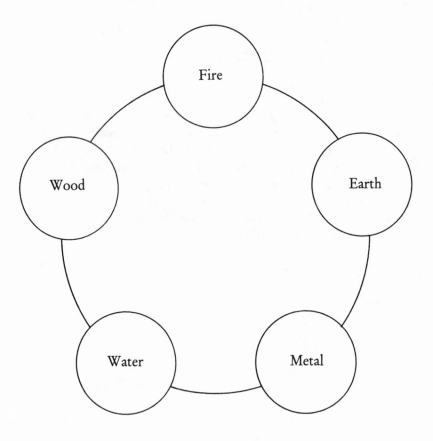

Figure 6: The five elements

II. Correspondences of the elements, cosmos, and humankind

Corres-pondence	Element				
	Wood	**Fire**	**Earth**	**Metal**	**Water**
planet	Jupiter	Mars	Saturn	Venus	Mercury
direction	east	south	the center	west	north
season	spring	summer	late summer	autumn	winter
influence	wind	heat	dampness	dryness	cold
time of day	dawn	noon	afternoon	evening	night
evolution	birth	growth	transfor-mation	decline	stagnation: death = new life
symbolic animal	dog	horse	ox	hen	pig
mythical animal	dragon	sun	bird	tiger	moon or tortoise
metal	tin	iron	lead	copper	mercury
meat	chicken	sheep	ox	horse	pork
grain	sesame rice	wheat	yellow millet, corn	oats and rice	black beans
number	8	7	5	9	6
color	green	red	yellow	white	black
tone	jiao = 3rd	zhi = 4th	gong = 1st	shang = 2nd	yu = 5th
flavor	acid or sour	bitter	sweet & mild	hot, spicy, acrid	salty
organ	liver	heart pericardium	spleen-pancreas	lung	kidney
bowel	gallbladder	small intestine, triple burner	stomach	large intestine	bladder
orifice	eye	the 7 orifices	mouth	nose	ear, urinary meatus, rectum
sense	sight	taste	touch	smell	hearing
tissue	muscles	blood vessels	flesh	skin	bone
emotion	anger	joy	reflection	sadness	fear
psychic principle	hun	shen	yi	po	zhi

The Five Elements and the Twelve Organs

Because man is viewed as a microcosmic representation of the macrocosm, our viscera, visceral functions and meridians are classified according to the five elements. Each of the elements is associated with two organ functions and meridians in a yin-yang relationship. The relationship of the five elements and the twelve organs and meridians are illustrated as follows.[14]

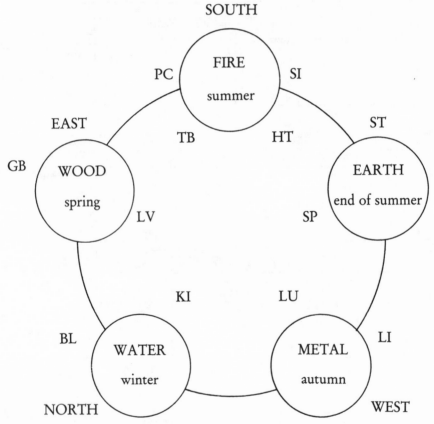

Figure 7: The five elements and the twelve organs

The element wood groups together the meridians and functions of the liver (a full organ and thus yin) and the gallbladder (a hollow organ and thus yang). Metal groups the meridians and functions of the lung (yin) and the large intestine (yang). Fire groups not two but four functions and meridians. Imperial fire brings together the heart (yin) and the small intestine (yang), and the fire ministers that serve the heart (the autonomic nervous system), the pericardium meridian (yin) and the triple burner (yang), the sympathetic and parasympathetic systems. Water groups together the meridians and functions of kidney-adrenal-gonad (yin) and bladder (yang). Earth groups together the meridians and functions of the spleen-pancreas and stomach.

Dynamics of the Five Elements

The five elements are not as static as their classification in tables implies. On the contrary, there is motion to and from the elements, as well as between them.

Law of equilibrium within an element. For each element there exists a dynamic equilibrium between the yin and yang functions, as well as the zang and fu organs. A disturbance in one results in a disturbance in the other. For example, if the gallbladder meridian has an excess of energy, then the liver meridian is empty, and vice versa. The disturbance can be corrected at the level of the meridians through the intermediary of secondary meridians called *connecting luo* meridians. These meridians play a role in the pre-terminal anastomosis (convening) of meridians and allow the passage of an overflow from one meridian to another. On each meridian a special point opens so that the overflow of energy may pass toward its coupled meridian. This point is called the *luo* point. Another point, the *yuan* point, accepts the overflow. To induce the excess energy to pass from one to the other, the acupuncturist pricks the luo point of the meridian with an excess of energy and the yuan point of the meridian with insufficient energy.

The following figure illustrates the equilibrium between two coupled meridians, the liver and gallbladder. To equilibrate the excess energy in the gallbladder meridian and the insufficient energy in the liver meridian, the acupuncturist will prick the luo point of the gallbladder meridian and the yuan point of the liver meridian. Thus, when the activity of a meridian is in excess, the meridian to which it is coupled will be insufficient, or vice versa.[15]

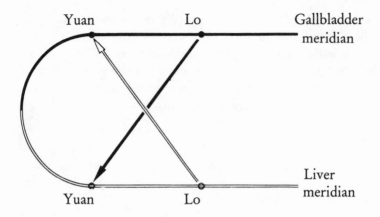

Figure 8: Luo and yuan points

Laws of equilibrium between the elements. Beyond the law of equilibrium of functions in the same element, there exist two other laws of interdependence that relate functions between the elements: the mother-son law and the law of domination and repression.

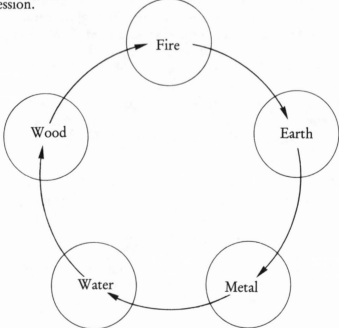

Figure 9: The mother-son law

The mother-son law is based on the normal succession of phenomena in nature, for example, the seasons. After spring comes summer, then at the end of summer comes autumn, and finally winter. In acupuncture this law is reflected in the relationships among the visceral functions: after the lung comes the kidney, then the liver, then the heart, the spleen, and finally the lung again. This law of succession is like a familial relationship, and thus it is called the mother-son law. The liver represents the mother of the heart, the heart is the mother of the spleen, etc. Each element engenders or nourishes the element it precedes in the indicated cycle. This relation is considered to be internal because the succession occurs physiologically rather than externally in the meridians of the skin.[15]

The law of domination and repression takes into account both equilibrium and alternation. Spring is opposed to autumn, winter to summer, the end of summer to winter and spring simultaneously. In acupuncture this is expressed physiologically as relationships of opposition between organ functions: the lung is opposed to the liver, the kidney to the heart, etc. This law operates in both directions, giving a cycle of domination and a cycle of repression.

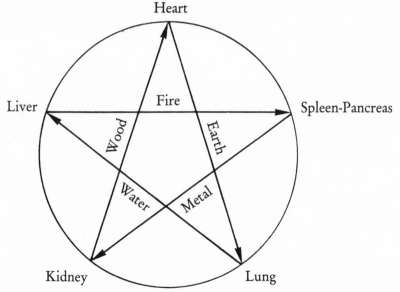

Figure 10: Cycle of Domination

The lung dominates the liver, which dominates the spleen, which dominates the kidney, which dominates the heart, which dominates the lung. Inversely, the liver can turn against the lung, the lung against the heart, the heart against the kidney, the kidney against the spleen, the spleen against the liver. A diseased heart can bring on a failure of the lung, which is what is termed in Western medicine a "cardiac lung." The diseased lung can, in turn, provoke a failure in the heart, which is called "chronic pulmonary heart."

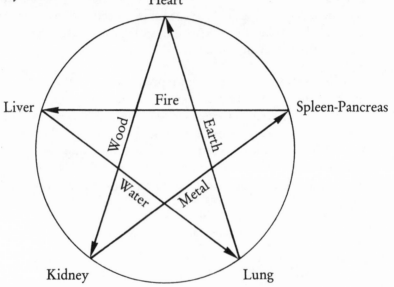

Figure 11: Cycle of Repression

To sum up, the Chinese express the cycle of domination allegorically:

> Wood feeds the fire that produces cinders [earth].
> In its core earth engenders metal that can be liquefied [water].
> In its turn, water makes vegetation [wood] grow.

For the cycle of repression:

> Wood eats the earth,
> the earth dams water,
> water extinguishes the fire,
> fire founds metal,
> metal cuts down wood."

The Five Elements and Psychosomatics

The five elements have another essential application, which is the classification of human behavior — intellectual, psychological, and physiological — into types or constitutions. According to the theories of Chinese acupuncture, the constitution of an individual can be defined as the inherited vulnerability of one or more of the twelve organ-meridian systems of the body. This vulnerability predisposes the body to specific illnesses, to a degree determined by the intensity of the organ weakness.

Because the Chinese believed that all that exists in the cosmos is mirrored in humankind, they classified human beings via the five elements, in the same way that they classified physical phenomena. In the *Nei Jing* the relationship is expressed clearly:

> The five kingdoms or five elements — wood, fire, earth, metal and water — embrace all the phenomena of nature; this is a symbolism that is equally applicable to man.
>
> Persons of the wood type have a greenish complexion, a long physique, wide shoulders, small hands and feet; they are workers.
>
> Persons of the fire type have a reddish complexion, small head, pointed chin, and rounded back, shoulders, hips, and stomach. They also have small hands and feet, they walk quickly, they are nimble and active and have much energy. They are prudent but sensitive, and often do not keep their word. Their life span is in general rather short.
>
> Persons of the earth type have a yellowish complexion, a large head and round face, fleshy back and shoulders, fat thighs and stomach, small hands and feet. They are calm, generous, not very ambitious, and do not seek honors.
>
> Persons of the metal type have a white complexion, small head, narrow shoulders, small hands and feet. They are unpretentious, meticulous, and clairvoyant; they make good judges.

33

Persons of the water type have a blackish complexion, large head, narrow shoulders, fat belly. They like movement, their vertebral column is longer than normal, and often they are not honest (9).

These descriptions constitute the basis of the five psychosomatic behaviors of acupuncture that correspond to the five constitutions defined by the five elements. One should not, however, take these classifications too literally. Each type has countless variations, because all the correspondences that are contained in the element come into play to define the constitution, those of the organ functions and the meridians as much as the accessory functions.

For example, the earth type exhibits a short figure and round face, and the character is indolent and amorphous. These structural and behavioral aspects are related to a constitutional weakness of the spleen-pancreas organ and the stomach, from which comes the problem of excess weight leading to obesity. This condition in turn predisposes to diabetes, aggravated by the tendency to indulge in sweets and suffer frequent and sudden attacks of hunger. Such subjects are also sensitive to humidity, which can provoke edema, water retention, and rheumatism, because the spleen, linked to the skin, regulates the collagen metabolism as well as the articulations. This example only begins to reveal the extent to which the correspondences between the meridians and organ functions add to our understanding of the variety of human behavior. This we can confirm by comparison to the behavioral descriptions developed in our modern culture.

Chapter 3

The Trace Elements and Diathetic Medicine

The five characteristic constitutions and their association with specific behavior patterns, vulnerabilities, symptoms, and illnesses, can be found in another, Occidental, medical system of classification: oligotherapy, or functional diathetic medicine, a method originating with Jacques Menetrier that distinguishes five groups of diseases termed diatheses. The data that Menetrier collected in an experimental and empirical fashion over the years of his research coincide with the principles of grouping in the classification based on the five elements developed by the ancient Chinese physicians. This apparent coincidence demonstrates the fact that specific behaviors exist in people independent of culture. As such, it is not surprising that comparisons can be made between systems that attempt to group behavior patterns.

Diathetic medicine defines diatheses as constitutional susceptibilities or terrains that are akin to the Chinese concept of constitution. Menetrier used this approach in speaking of psychosomatic personalities (28). Those who propound the adaptiveness of mental and behavioral processes further describe the diatheses as pathologic changes that occur in an individual according to his or her particular constitution. This passage or change from one state to another implies a dynamic motion. The idea of dynamic motion also exists in acupuncture in the concept of the five elements, via the laws of generation, domination, and repression.

In diathetic medicine, the five diatheses are grouped around a specific trace element. Each trace element is a metal collected in infinitely small amounts, or two or three metals in the form of gluconate, to form an original medication that is prescribed to correct the set of problems defined in the diatheses.[17]

The correspondence of diatheses in the functional medicine of Menetrier with the five constitutions is described diagrammatically as follows:

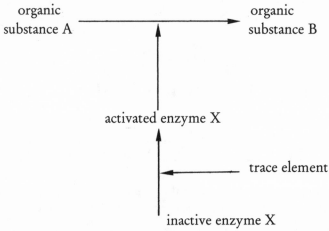

Figure 12: Mode of action of the trace elements on enzymatic reactions

Diathesis I, called the *allergic* or *arthritic* diathesis, corresponds to the Chinese constitution wood. Treatment for this type includes manganese as the trace element, either alone or in association with sulfur.

Diathesis II, called the *hyposthenic* diathesis, corresponds to the Chinese constitution metal. Manganese and copper together are the trace elements associated with this diathesis.

Diathesis III, called the *dystonic* diathesis, corresponds to the Chinese constitution fire. Treatment includes manganese in association with cobalt.

Diathesis IV, called the *anergic* diathesis, corresponds to the Chinese constitution water. Treatment includes the association of copper, gold, and silver.

Diathesis V, referred to as either the *pituitary-gonadal* or *pituitary-pancreatic disadaptation,* corresponds to the Chinese constitution earth. The pituitary-gonadal disadaptation is treated by zinc and copper, and the pituitary-pancreatic disadaptation by zinc, nickel, and cobalt together. These correspondences are summarized in the following table.

Correspondence of the Diatheses with the Chinese Constitutions			
Diathesis	*Trace element*	*Chinese constitution*	*Functions and meridians*
Allergic or Arthritic	manganese and sulfur	wood	gallbladder liver
Hyposthenic	manganese-copper	metal	large intestine lung
Dystonic	manganese-cobalt	fire	small intestine heart triple burner pericardium
Anergic	copper-gold-silver	water	bladder kidney
Pituitary-gonadal or Pituitary-pancreatic Disadaptation	zinc-copper or zinc-nickel-cobalt	earth	stomach spleen-pancreas

The mechanism by which the trace elements exert their effects is unknown. The results of some experimental investigations indicate that these elements may act by liberating the same element already present in the body but incapable of acting because it is enclosed by large molecules (chelation). The degree of chelation present in an individual depends on the degree of natural tendency toward chelation; it is a function of one's constitution. Other factors contributing to chelation include elemental contaminants in the environment that are respired, foodstuffs containing large amounts of chemicals (pesticides, antibiotics, chemical fertilizers, etc.), and the absorption of various chemical medications containing chelating agents. A sedentary life and stress are also contributory.

The effect of the introduction of the trace elements in small doses can be dramatic, since these elements liberate and facilitate the metabolic pathways dependent on them. In effect they activate many of the specific enzymes that play a role in the transformation of one substance to another, acting in the role of catalyst to make the enzyme operational.

Each group of chemical reactions, however different and apparently foreign, and however distant from each other in various tissues, has a precise relationship with a specific trace element. Each trace element is also associated with two acupuncture meridians and their respective functions.

One advantage of the therapeutic application of the trace elements is ease of delivery. Doses are given one to three times a week, with the aim of correcting a particular diathetic problem. The trace element is taken either singly or alternately with the trace elements of other diathetic states, depending on the complexity of the disturbance.

Another advantage lies in the ability of the trace elements to correct problems that, although minor, are nevertheless troublesome, such as a tendency to be bothered by hiccups, to be too long in getting to sleep, to have moderate morning nausea, to experience a "drained" feeling at midmorning, or to suffer from small hunger pangs that occur throughout the day. One is disinclined to take prescription medicines for such symptoms, or undergo extensive acupuncture treatment. The trace elements are the mildest of the three choices of treatment available, and the most logical for this type of problem.

The treatment of an individual by the application of trace elements should be determined by a physician knowledgeable in diathetic medicine. Not only will the treatment thus be precisely tailored to the individual, but such a physician can also take advantage of the application of the secondary but complementary trace elements, such as magnesium, phosphorus, iodine, cobalt, potassium, aluminum, etc.

Perhaps the most important advantage that results from a knowledge of diatheses and the Chinese constitutions is that the trace elements, carefully prescribed according to the constitution of the individual, potentiate to a remarkable degree the action of acupuncture and prolong the effects of the acupuncture session.

Finally, prescription of the trace elements can be of prophylactic benefit, and can ward off the occurrence of an illness if taken at the time of the onset of the earliest warning symptoms.

Chapter 4

The Character Types of Gaston Berger

The third system involved in our synthesis of complementary modalities comes from psychology. It is a system of typologic classification into eight character types.

The first typologic model of psychological behavior proposed in the West came from Galen, a Greek physician who lived in the first century A.D. He defined four basic temperaments: enthusiastic, sanguine, melancholic, and phlegmatic. Since that time, many behavioral models have been set forth. Broadly speaking, we may categorize these models as two approaches: the subjective, introspective psychology represented by the depth psychology of Jung and the psychoanalytic theories of Freud and the post-Freudian schools; and the objective, experimental, and quantitative psychology that includes comparative psychology and pathologic psychology, represented by such groups as the Dutch school of Heymans and Wiersma, and their French disciple, Le Senne.

Gaston Berger, a psychologist from Marseilles, was the student of Le Senne (2). Together they developed the character types that were initially introduced by Heymans and Wiersma. In the process of their development, Berger created a test for determining the degree to which emotivity, activity, and resonance were expressed in individuals.

The Eight Character Types

The degree to which emotivity, activity, and resonance are united determines eight character types:

The Eight Character Types		
Classification		*Characteristic*
E.A.P.	Emotive, Active, Primary	Enthusiastic
E.nA.P.	Emotive, non-Active, Primary	Nervous
E.A.S.	Emotive, Active, Secondary	Passionate
E.nA.S.	Emotive, non-Active, Secondary	Sentimental
nE.A.P.	non-Emotive, Active, Primary	Sanguine
nE.nA.P.	non-Emotive, non-Active, Primary	Amorphous
nE.A.S.	non-Emotive, Active, Secondary	Phlegmatic
nE.nA.S.	non-Emotive, non-Active, Secondary	Apathetic

These eight character types correspond to eight precise types of behavior, and were first described in detail by Le Senne and later by Berger in his book, *Practical Treatise of Analysis of Character*. In this work the author described a test composed of thirty questions, ten bearing on emotivity, ten on activity and ten on resonance. Six other secondary aspects of character were introduced, with ten supplementary questions for each aspect.

Emotivity. This measures the extent to which a person is moved emotionally. It determines the degree of excitability, sensitivity, nervousness — the affective nature of the individual. Persons are considered highly emotive if their reaction to a stimulus is greater than is warranted by the intensity of the stimulus — for example, jumping at the slightest noise. On the affective level an emotive person will exhibit dramatic changes in behavior over little or nothing. More often than others the emotive person is highly reactive to physical surroundings or internal impressions. They are hypersensitive, never ceasing to feel, to desire, fear; to be enthused, astonished, indignant; to rejoice, to hope or despair. "A person who is bothered by trifles we call emotive," says Berger. "The emotive person is more violently moved than the majority of persons in the same or similar circumstances. Such persons are troubled by motives that they are the first to recognize as not worth the pain." The emotive person "takes everything to heart."

Contrarily, a non-emotive or poorly emotive person is troubled only in rare circumstances. He or she does not startle easily, is even-tempered, indeed indifferent, and maintains his or her composure easily.

The emotive person, in the system of classification of Jung, corresponds to the feeling type; the non-emotive person to the thinking type. The remark of Vauvenargues is apt for the non-emotive type of person: "Reason knows not the interests of the heart."

Activity. This behavioral characteristic is common in a person who not only does a great deal but who has "the disposition to act readily," Berger comments. This person does not have to force him- or herself to perform, for there is a readiness to always do something. For the active person difficulties and obstacles are stimulating; nothing is put off until the next day that can be done the same day. As a consequence the active person feels bad if there is nothing to do; he or she does not tolerate well remaining unoccupied.

The non-active person must force him- or herself to act. Only by force of necessity, by duty, or a kind of automatism is an action taken. Activity occurs sporadically and in bursts, and is usually motivated by something pleasurable. Given the opportunity the non-active person will procrastinate, especially when the task is one of drudgery.

The active person corresponds to the sthenic (sturdy) in other typologic systems, and the non-active to the asthenic (weak). Corman notes that active persons possess energetic facial features, whereas non-active persons are characterized by more sluggish, sunken features, or features that are softer or rounder.

Resonance. This behavioral characteristic describes reaction. Reaction to a stimulus is either direct and immediate, what Berger calls "primary resonance," or is indirect and deferred, "secondary resonance." According to Berger, "the subject whose capacity for reaction is primary is under the influence of present events. This person lives in the present, and it is the present from which the necessary information for reaction to stimuli is extracted. For the person whose nature is secondary, the past plays a significant role.

It does not merely support the present but predetermines it, orients and designs it in advance" (3).

Resonance analyses place careful consideration on the delay between the stimulus and the response. The response can be immediate, and can be traced along the reflex arc of the medulla that, by the retreat reflex, protects the individual against pain, such as from a burn. Corman aptly describes this pattern by the statement, "The action is short-circuited." It is the reaction, says this writer, of "impulsive" subjects, of "first movement."

The response to a stimulus, however, whether it be intellectual or verbal, affective or one of action, can also be deferred. Here the action is not short-circuited, but is traced through the cerebral model of nervous reactions, passing through all the associative areas. It is a deferred or delayed secondary reaction, as if the brain had deliberately slowed the resultant action in some way.

The behavior of the primary person will be spontaneous, natural, impulsive, indeed capricious, confident and credulous, and free of malice. This person will be unforesightful and live from day to day. By contrast, the behavior of the secondary type of person will be controlled or calculated and constrained. The confidence and credulity in the primary type turns to reserve and mistrust in the secondary type. The actions, emotions, and aims of this individual take into account the past, and there is a preoccupation with the future. This person is foreseeing. He or she does not forget past experiences. Such experiences mold his or her attitudes, or they are pondered inordinately, whether they be good or bad. The secondary type of person projects him- or herself into the distant future and realizes his or her aims by persistent effort.

The eight character types of Berger provide an appropriate model by which comparison can be made between behavior types established by modern Western psychology and those recognized by acupuncture. The character types described by Berger can be related to acupuncture meridians; the relationship can be demonstrated and experimentally verified. The correspondence exists not only with the ideas of ancient Chinese psychology, but also the hypothesis of central nervous system substances described in chapter 2. It is also connected with the psychosomatic constitutions and profiles that the Chinese defined in their earliest works.

Through a study of such correlations we can recognize the physical weakness of a person and relate it to his or her constitution.

Correlating Acupuncture Temperaments and the Eight Character Types of Berger

Recognition of the relationship between Chinese medical systems and characterologic analyses permits the health-conscious individual to undertake self-directed measures to improve well-being and to act preventively. It helps the acupuncturist to more precisely define the specific nature of the patient, as well as more accurately determine the energy disequilibrium in the meridians as a function of behavior. It permits the psychologist to determine the physiologic dimension of the patient, and in consequence, the degree of character differentiation. Similarly, a knowledge of this relationship offers investigators of the correlations between character and temperament a far more systematic vantage point from which to view the mind-body tandem.

To more exactly specify the psychological behaviors that are associated with each of the six temperaments specified by Chinese medicine, we can examine the correspondence that can be established between these temperaments and the eight character types described by Gaston Berger. As we have seen, the eight types are defined by variations in the three factors — activity, emotivity and resonance.

Activity is a function of yin and yang. Yang is synonymous with activity, mobility; yin is synonymous with inactivity, immobility. The *Nei Jing* states, "Subjects with excess yang have spirit and more rapid energy; these are people who speak fast, and who are active." Thus, the three yang types, Tai Yang, Yang Ming, Shao Yang, are the active types. The descriptions of Tai Yang and Shao Yang in the *Nei Jing* imply this; there is an apparent constitutional tendency in these types toward excess yang. Since yang is essentially synonymous with heat, these persons will not be susceptible to cold and will avoid heat.

Yin, synonymous with inactivity and coldness, categorizes the non-active types: Tai Yin, Shao Yin, Jue Yin. The natural disequilibrium that exists in persons of these types is a tendency toward an excess of yin, which is manifested by a more and more marked inhibition of activity and a susceptibility to cold.

Emotivity is the propensity to be easily emotionally stirred, and often or intensely is linked to the heart, the organ of the fire element. The sinologist Joseph Needham defines the Shen elaborated by the heart as "energy that determines emotive activity" (32). One can therefore suppose that all subjects who have a meridian belonging to the fire element will be emotive, and, in contrast, those without a meridian belonging to the fire element will not be emotive. The type determined by the heart meridian and its organ, Shao Yin, will be the most emotive.

Resonance determines the type of response to stimuli: direct, immediate, and spontaneous for the primary type; indirect, deferred, and reflected for the secondary type.

By analogy, the types of persons with a meridian belonging to the wood element, which is associated with springtime, yang growth, dawn, birth, and spontaneity, and whose gallbladder and liver meridians are respectively primary to their energy circulation, coincide closely with the primary type described by Corman as "impulsive" and "subjects of first movement" (11).

On the other hand, subjects with a meridian belonging to the water element, which is associated with winter, night, the apogee of yin, rest and immobility, and the kidney and bladder meridians, correspond closely with secondary, slow, deferred, nonspontaneous, reflected activity.

Persons with meridians between these two extremes will lie between the primary and secondary types. Those persons determined by the metal element, which is associated with the season autumn, the period of withdrawal in nature, are inclined to be more secondary. The *Nei Jing* states, "The three months of autumn evoke a leveling-off period. One wishes to be more sedentary to alleviate the rigors of autumn. One refrains from aberrant thoughts so that the lung remains pure"(20).

To recapitulate the relationship between the types defined by Berger and those defined by acupuncture, we have:

Berger Type	Acupuncture Type
E.A.P.	Enthusiastic with Shao Yang
E.nA.P.	Nervous with Jue Yin
E.A.S.	Passionate with Tai Yang
E.nA.S.	Sentimental with Shao Yin
nE.A.P.	Sanguine with Yang Ming
nE.nA.P.	Amorphous with Tai Yin
nE.A.S.	Phlegmatic with Yang Ming
nE.nA.S.	Apathetic with Tai Yin

This correspondence may be seen graphically as follows:

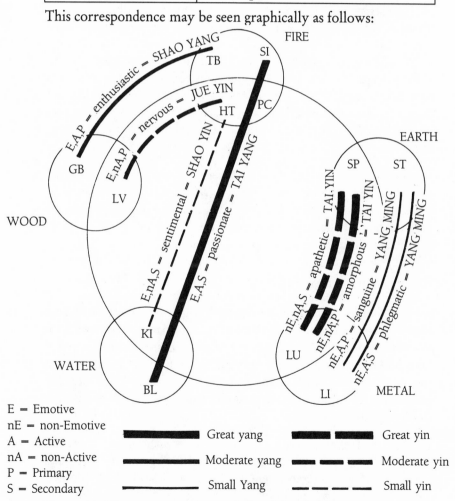

Figure 13: The temperaments and the eight character types

47

Alternation of the primary and secondary types between earth and metal results in two divisions for the Yang Ming and Tai Yin meridians. This division makes four possibilities that, added to the four other meridian types, compose the correspondences with the eight character types of Berger. The equilibrium is maintained, since there are four emotive and four non-emotive types, four primary and four secondary types, four active and four non-active types.

There is a close correspondence between the two systems of classification. The Shao Yang person, for example, is characterized by behavior that is partly determined by the gallbladder meridian and function, and partly determined by the yang viscera associated with the wood element. When excessive, yang is psychologically reflected as aggressivity. It is an anger that can sometimes be violent, even to the extreme of outbursts of blind rage. This pattern corresponds closely with the enthusiastic character type of Berger, a type also described as choleric. They like to begin projects but never finish them, like to act, and greatly enjoy making decisions.

In acupuncture, the gallbladder is the arbiter, the decision-maker. The *Nei Jing* even states, "When the gallbladder is in excess the person makes decisions easily, and is impetuous; or, on the contrary, if the gallbladder has insufficient energy in its meridian, then the person is incapable of making decisions." Berger says of the enthusiastic type that such persons are full of vitality, are impetuous, are readily revolutionary, bellicose, and trainers of men. Characteristically they are courageous and audacious. The ancient Chinese attached the name "large vesicle" (vesicle here referring to the gallbladder) to persons abundantly endowed with this character (12). An ancient story describes a Chinese warrior who had triumphed over his adversary in combat. He tore open the opponent's body with a knife, extracted, then ate the gallbladder to acquire for himself the bellicose virtues of his vanquished enemy (12).

The correspondence is equally close for the other character types. The Shao Yin, associated with the heart meridian, corresponds to the sentimental character described by Berger. This person is hyperemotive and hypersensitive. The Jue Yin type, whose physical vulnerability takes the form of a weakness of the liver, rendering the person anxious, irritable and nervous, corresponds to the nervous character type of Berger.

Tai Yang is the greatest yang, endowed with the greatest capacity for action, with the highest authority due to the excess of *zhi* (will). At the same time there is great sensitivity due to the emotivity conferred by the small intestine meridian belonging to the element fire and coupled with the heart. This temperament corresponds to the passionate character type, described by Berger as "endowed with great strength, and inclined to take part in the most raging battles."

The Tai Yin type can be either primary or secondary. If primary, the person is more determined by the earth element than by metal. Morphologically the person will be corpulent, of short stature, non-active and non-emotive. His or her attitude toward life is one of carelessness. The Tai Yin-earth type corresponds perfectly with the amorphous type of Berger. We have seen that persons of earth type were described in the *Nei Jing* as devoid of ambition, calm, generous, and disinclined to seek honors. It is exactly these words that Berger used to describe the amorphous type.

If the Tai Yin type is secondary, then metal is the determining element. This person is withdrawn, prey to reflection, to pessimism, to the mood and movement of autumn, non-active and non-emotive, disinclined to be moved by others, and tending toward misanthropy. The Tai Yin-metal type corresponds in all regards to the apathetic type described by Berger, who sees this person as "somber, taciturn, closed, secretive, tenacious in his antipathies." The *Nei Jing* describes the Tai Yin type as "cunning and treacherous. The facial aspect is always somber. The person is extremely polite, bowing before everyone. The stature is tall with long femurs."

The Yang Ming type, which can also be either primary or secondary, corresponds to Yang Ming-earth, a type that is sanguine, yang and active, a replica of the amorphous type. This character also corresponds to Yang Ming-metal, a type that is phlegmatic, productive, calm, self-controlled, non-emotive, governed almost exclusively by reason.

The above examples illustrate briefly a few of the correspondences that can be drawn between the two systems of classification. More detailed comparisons have been developed elsewhere (33).

Chapter 5

Tests for Determining Your Character Type

There are four tests in this chapter. Each will tell you something about yourself. Taken together they can help you form a more complete and useful idea of your character. First, you will acquire a clear understanding of your primary and secondary constitutional characteristics: fire, earth, metal, water, or wood. Next, you will acquire a reliable assessment of your primary and secondary temperaments: Tai Yang, Shao Yang, Yang Ming, Tai Yin, Shao Yin, or Jue Yin. Then, by synthesizing your primary and secondary constitutions and temperaments, you will be able to form a complex, many-leveled, and useful guide for your own use.

In the following chapters you will read descriptions of each constitution and each temperament. This is also an experience that will help you confirm and understand what you have learned from the tests. First, read these descriptions yourself, noting what parts of each description apply to you. You may also ask your friends to read these chapters and chose the constitution and temperament they feel best describes you. Their image of you may point to traits that you have missed. With all this information in mind you can then read the preventive and developmental ideas given for each temperament. Equipped with this more precise understanding you will be well prepared to examine the many complementary health care and self-development ideas that you have already learned, and the many you will hear about in the future, with some clear goals in mind.

A full synthesis of all the information concerning your constitution and temperament will take some time, thought, and experience. Begin with the basic information. Then study the preceding chapters again. This time pay close attention to the details of each system that apply to you.

The first test is a simple and reliable means of determining whether your body evidences a predominance of yin or yang. Of course, there are shades and variations, gradations of the tendency toward yin or yang. These gradations are expressed more exactly by the temperaments. Yet, knowing your general tendency toward one of these poles allows you to examine yourself as active or inactive, primary or secondary, one of the yin temperaments, or one of the yang temperaments.

The next test examines the structure of your hand. Take your time and consider each question carefully. If you question your own answer, ask a friend. When you have completed the test, your combined score will tell you the predominance of the constitutional types you evidence.

The third test asks you to select from a list of common childhood problems those that affected you when you were a child. Most of us have fairly vague memories of our early illnesses, so you may want to speak to a parent, or even your family physician. The results of this test extend and confirm the analysis of constitutional type.

The fourth test is the "Characterologic Evaluation 40." This is much like the personality surveys that you were given in school. Like those tests it uses questions that you identify as describing you accurately to create a picture, in this case a picture of your specific temperament. Unlike those tests, you will have an opportunity to understand and use the evaluation. It is possible to use the primary and secondary temperaments determined by this test for many purposes. However, at first, concentrate on the characteristics discussed in chapter 6. When you feel you have mastered this information, you can use the relationships between your temperament and specific acupuncture concepts: meridians, *zang* and *fu* organs, the Chinese clock, and seasonal biorhythms, to understand more about your physiological and psychological nature. This information will also help you understand ideas concerning disease and the five elements. It can help you chose from among the many techniques of self-healing and self-development — such as tai chi, qi gong, yoga, meditation, massage, and diet — the methods that are of the greatest benefit for you.

Hand Analysis Tests

Is your hand yin or yang?

The first test helps determine the yin-yang form of your hand. Respond to each question. If your answer is yes, enter one point in the specified yin or yang column. If your answer is no, enter one point in the yin or yang column **not** specified. For example, if your handshake is soft and wavering, a yes answer to the first question, put one point in the "yin" column and nothing in the "yang" column. On the other hand, if your handshake is not soft, a "no" answer to that question, put one point in the "yang" column and nothing in the "yin" column. If you cannot categorize your answer as a definite yes, assign one-half point (0.5) to each the yin score and the yang score.

Is Your Hand Yin or Yang?			
Question	Yin/Yang	Score	
		Yin	Yang
Is your handshake soft and wavering?	Yes = Yin		1
Is your handshake firm and vigorous?	Yes = Yang		1
Are your hands cold?	Yes = Yin		1
Are your hands warm?	Yes = Yang		1
Are your hands pale, yellowish or blue?	Yes = Yin		1
Are your hands red or well colored?	Yes = Yang		1
Total your scores in each column	**Total**		6

Structural analysis of your hand

What is the overall form of your hand? First, look at each of the five pictures of hands shown on the following pages. There is one hand for each of the five hand morphologies — wood, fire, earth, metal, water. Choose the shape that most clearly matches your hand. These are general pictures so no one's hand will match the picture perfectly. Choose the one that most closely resembles your hand. If in doubt, ask a friend to confirm your choice. If you think your hand and a picture match completely, or nearly so, score 5 points at the box provided following the first question, "Hand Characteristics," of the appropriate picture. If the match is partial, score 2.5 points for each of the two pictures that are the best matches. Score no more than two pictures as a match.

The shape of your fingernails. Next, check the descriptions for each of the five types of hand morphologies — wood, fire, earth, metal, water. Look at all the pictures first, read all the descriptions, then choose the shape that most clearly matches your fingernails. If the match is complete, or nearly so, score three points at the box provided next to the second question, "Fingernail Characteristics." If the match is partial, score 1.5 points for the two most notable matches. Score no more than two partial matches. Although the shape of the fingernail generally matches the overall proportions of the hand, there are sometimes exceptions (see page 58, the metal hand).

The shape of your fingers. Again, look at all the pictures and read all the descriptions first. Check the descriptions for each of the five types — wood, fire, earth, metal, water. Choose the shape that most clearly matches your fingers. If the match is complete, or nearly so, score one point at the box provided next to the third question, "Finger Characteristics." If you perceive your fingers to match characteristics of two or more of different types, score one point for each. For example, if your fingers are long and zig-zag (metal), and spatulate and soft (water), score one point for metal and one point for water. Score one point for every match. However, if you think your fingers match three or more of the finger shapes, have a friend confirm your choices.

Specific signs that match your hands. Again, begin by looking at all five pictures and reading each description. Check the descriptions for each of the five hand morphologies — wood, fire, earth, metal, water. Choose the sign that most clearly matches your hand. If the match is complete, or nearly so, score one point at the box provided at the "Specific Characteristics" area. If your hand matches characteristics of two or more of the different types, score one point for each. Again, if you are considering multiple matches, check with a friend.

The Wood Hand

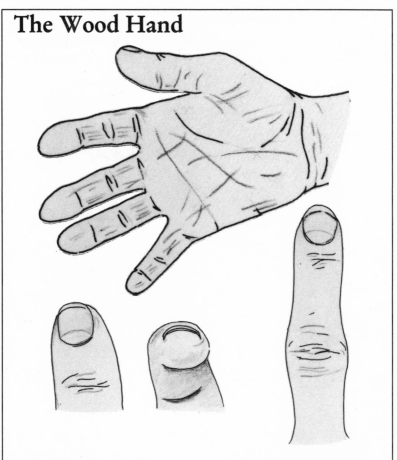

1. Hand Characteristics:
5 pts. full match; 2.5 pts. partial: [5]
Well-proportioned

2. Fingernail Characteristics:
3 pts. full match; 1.5 pts. partial: [3]
Normally convex curvature
Yang: hard, strong,
    with sizeable moons
Yin: brittle, fragile, bitten

3. Finger Characteristics:
1 pt. full match; 1 pt. 2nd (equal) match: [1]
proportionally normal length
knotted joints (due to
    sparse flesh on dorsal side)

4. Specific Characteristics:
1 pt. full match; 1 pt. 2n'd (equal) match: [1]
Numerous lines on palm and
    ventral surface
Criss-cross grooves on palm

The Fire Hand

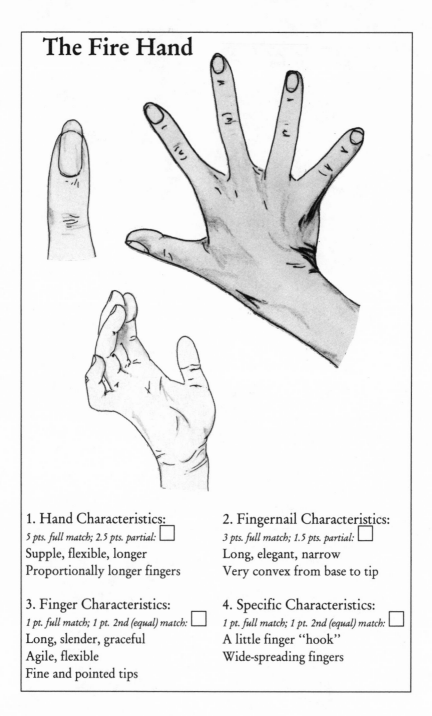

1. Hand Characteristics:
5 pts. full match; 2.5 pts. partial: ☐
Supple, flexible, longer
Proportionally longer fingers

2. Fingernail Characteristics:
3 pts. full match; 1.5 pts. partial: ☐
Long, elegant, narrow
Very convex from base to tip

3. Finger Characteristics:
1 pt. full match; 1 pt. 2nd (equal) match: ☐
Long, slender, graceful
Agile, flexible
Fine and pointed tips

4. Specific Characteristics:
1 pt. full match; 1 pt. 2nd (equal) match: ☐
A little finger "hook"
Wide-spreading fingers

The Earth Hand

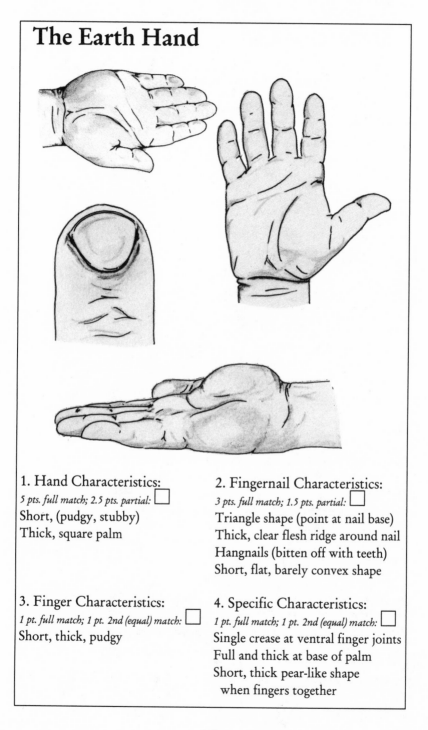

1. Hand Characteristics:
5 pts. full match; 2.5 pts. partial: ☐
Short, (pudgy, stubby)
Thick, square palm

2. Fingernail Characteristics:
3 pts. full match; 1.5 pts. partial: ☐
Triangle shape (point at nail base)
Thick, clear flesh ridge around nail
Hangnails (bitten off with teeth)
Short, flat, barely convex shape

3. Finger Characteristics:
1 pt. full match; 1 pt. 2nd (equal) match: ☐
Short, thick, pudgy

4. Specific Characteristics:
1 pt. full match; 1 pt. 2nd (equal) match: ☐
Single crease at ventral finger joints
Full and thick at base of palm
Short, thick pear-like shape
   when fingers together

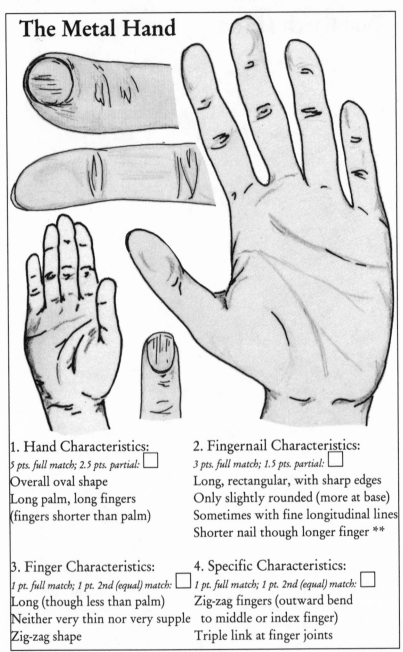

The Metal Hand

1. Hand Characteristics:

5 pts. full match; 2.5 pts. partial: ☐

Overall oval shape
Long palm, long fingers
(fingers shorter than palm)

2. Fingernail Characteristics:

3 pts. full match; 1.5 pts. partial: ☐

Long, rectangular, with sharp edges
Only slightly rounded (more at base)
Sometimes with fine longitudinal lines
Shorter nail though longer finger **

3. Finger Characteristics:

1 pt. full match; 1 pt. 2nd (equal) match: ☐

Long (though less than palm)
Neither very thin nor very supple
Zig-zag shape

4. Specific Characteristics:

1 pt. full match; 1 pt. 2nd (equal) match: ☐

Zig-zag fingers (outward bend
to middle or index finger)
Triple link at finger joints

*** In these cases the last or distal joint of the finger may be shaped
something like a drumstick - wider at the head. If your fingernails
match this shape either partially or completely, score as "metal."*

The Water Hand

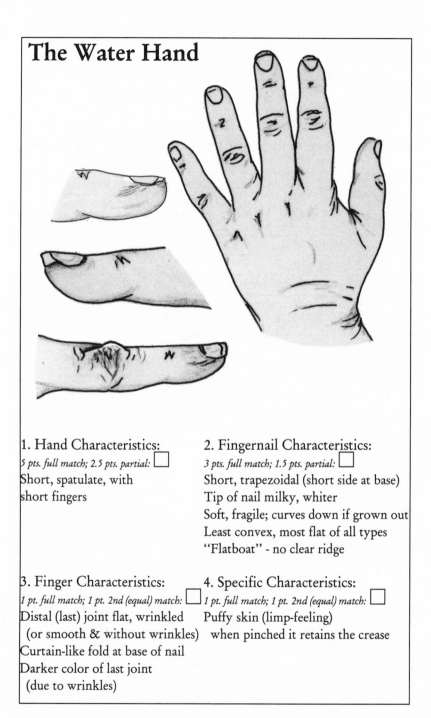

1. Hand Characteristics:
5 pts. full match; 2.5 pts. partial: ☐
Short, spatulate, with
short fingers

2. Fingernail Characteristics:
3 pts. full match; 1.5 pts. partial: ☐
Short, trapezoidal (short side at base)
Tip of nail milky, whiter
Soft, fragile; curves down if grown out
Least convex, most flat of all types
"Flatboat" - no clear ridge

3. Finger Characteristics:
1 pt. full match; 1 pt. 2nd (equal) match: ☐
Distal (last) joint flat, wrinkled
 (or smooth & without wrinkles)
Curtain-like fold at base of nail
Darker color of last joint
 (due to wrinkles)

4. Specific Characteristics:
1 pt. full match; 1 pt. 2nd (equal) match: ☐
Puffy skin (limp-feeling)
 when pinched it retains the crease

Hand Analysis Results

Go back to each of the five hand pictures. Using the table below, enter the scores for each question for each of the five morphologic types. Add each column, wood, fire, earth, metal, water, putting the sum in the **Total** line. Remember, no characteristic should have scores in more than two of the five element columns.

	Table One: Hand Analysis Results					
Total Points	**Characteristics**	*Elements*				
		Wood	*Fire*	*Earth*	*Metal*	*Water*
5	1. Overall shape					
3	2. Shape of nail					
1	3. Finger characteristics					
1	4. Specific characteristics					
10	**Total**					

The First Synthesis — Hand Characteristics

Hand shapes relate to constitution and temperament. If the results of the first test shows that your hand is more yin than yang, your primary temperament should be yin: Shao Yin, Jue Yin, Tai Yin-earth or Tai Yin-metal. If you hand is more yang than yin, your primary temperament should be Yang: Shao Yang, Tai Yang, Yang Ming-earth or Yang Ming-metal. Hands that have predominantly wood and fire shapes will be associated with Shao Yang or Jue Yin. Hands with fire and water shapes will be associated with Tai Yang or Shao Yin. Hands with earth and metal shapes will be associated with the Yang Ming and Tai Yin temperaments.

There are exceptions to these generalities. The metal hand may correspond equally well with the metal or earth types (Yang Ming-metal or Yang Ming-earth). The earth hand may correspond equally well with the earth or metal types (Tai Yin-earth or Tai Yin-metal). Also, the earth hand may be found with subjects of the Tai Yang passionate temperament.

Comparing the yin-yang predominance of your hand with the constitution-temperament correlations will give you an idea of the probable predominance of your temperament. For example, if your hand is yin and you have a higher hand score for water, then your probable temperament would be Shao Yin — the yin of water.

Constitution	Yang Temperament	Yin Temperament
Fire	Tai Yang/Small Intest.	Shao Yin/Heart
	Shao Yang/Triple Burner	Jue Yin/Pericardium
Earth	Yang Ming-Earth/Stomach	Tai Yin-Earth/Spleen
Metal	Yang Ming-Metal/Large Intest.	Tai Yin-Metal/Lung
Water	Tai Yang/Bladder	Shao Yin/Kidney
Wood	Shao Yang/Gallbladder	Jue Yin/Liver

Again, when you complete the Childhood Symptoms Test and the CE-40 Test, you shouldn't be surprised to see that your highest scores match the categorization of your hand. However, don't read ahead to look for the association of the questions to the temperaments. This might influence your answers. Take the tests in order, and fairly, for the most accurate results.

Childhood Symptoms Test

Reviewing your childhood symptoms or illnesses will further help to determine your constitutional type. First, go through the entire list of childhood illnesses and check (✓) each illness that you experienced as a child. The questions are presented in alphabetical order so that you won't be tempted to answer based on your developing understanding and expectations. Chances are that just from reading the preceding chapters and scoring the first three tests you have begun to form an idea of both your constitution and temperament. On the following page you will find a table in which you can score your "yes" answers to the questions. Each of the five sets of symptoms is arranged in accordance with the five elements. Add the points corresponding to the diseases that you suffered and enter a total for each element. Note that some of your answers are worth one point and others two points.

Question	Answer
Abnormal acetone levels in blood	☐
Bedwetting	☐
Bouts of uncontrollable sobbing	☐
Bronchitis	☐
Convulsions	☐
Digestive intolerances or allergies (eggs, chocolate)	☑
Dislocation of the testicle	☐
Epilepsy	☐
Fever to 104 °F	☐
Frequent hiccups or stomach complaints	☐
Fungal infections	☐
Hives or seasonal asthma	☐
Impetigo or boils	☑
Inflammation of the nose and throat, larynx, or trachea	☑
Intestinal parasites	☐
Late puberty	☐
Lateral curvature of the spine (scoliosis)	☐
Nail-biting	☑
Nearsightedness	☑
Orthostatic albuminuria	☐
Repeated anginas	☐
Severe ear inflammation	☑
Suppurating earaches or mastoiditis	☑
Thoracic pain (angina) - esp. in summer	☐
Viral hepatitis, neonatal jaundice, or fetal suffering	☐
Viral or bacterial infections	☑
Winter asthma	☐

Table Two: Evaluation of Childhood Symptoms

Element	Affliction	Points
Wood	Digestive intolerances or allergies (eggs, chocolate)	1
	Abnormal acetone levels in blood	1
	Nearsightedness	2
	Nail-biting	1
	Hives or seasonal asthma	1
	Viral hepatitis, neonatal jaundice, or fetal suffering	1
	Total Points	4
Metal	Inflammation of nose and throat, larynx, or trachea	1
	Severe ear inflammation without pus	1
	Bronchitis	1
	Winter asthma	2
	Lateral curvature of the spine (scoliosis)	1
	Bedwetting	1
	Total Points	2
Fire	Bouts of uncontrollable sobbing	1
	Fever to 104 °F	2
	Convulsions	1
	Epilepsy	1
	Thoracic pain (angina) - esp. in summer	2
	Total Points	0
Water	Orthostatic albuminuria	1
	Repeated anginas	2
	Suppurating earaches or mastoiditis	1
	Impetigo or boils	1
	Viral or bacterial infections	1
	Bedwetting	1
	Total Points	2
Earth	Intestinal parasites	1
	Fungal infections	1
	Frequent hiccups or stomach complaints	2
	Dislocation of the testicle	1
	Late puberty	1
	Bedwetting	1
	Total Points	0

Generally, people who are composed of three constitutions simultaneously reflect the constitution and character of the father and mother, or else just the parent with a similar constitutional complexity. Often, the morphology, characterology, vulnerabilities, and diseases of the parents are reflected in the child. Certain of the child's traits and associations can be recognized as those present in the father, and other, different traits and associations can be recognized as those present in the mother.[18]

The practitioners of diathetic medicine often examine the health history of the entire family. Some acupuncturists will do this as well, or ask questions concerning specific traits and illnesses. It is an interesting experience to give the tests to your parents, children, or even grandparents, to trace the constitutional and temperamental tendencies of your family.

The CE-40 Test

The "Characterologic Evaluation 40," abbreviated to "CE-40," provides a means for characterizing, in decreasing order of importance, a person's various tendencies. The questions included here were inspired by the test of Gex, first published in 1959 in his work, *Rapid Character Test*. The number of questions has changed to 40, rather than 38, and a number of statements have been made more precise. The scoring system used to evaluate the results has also been improved. You will use the scores from the CE-40 to determine character types, from most dominant to the least dominant.

Answers to the CE-40 Questionnaire should be marked on **Grid One**, page 68, by checking the appropriate box. Use the ratings below as a guide for choosing your response, giving only one answer for each question:

Test Ratings	
Rating & Score	Description
Very much: 10 points	If you think the sentence describes you completely or if you can largely identify with the statement.
Quite a bit: 5 points	If one part of the statement is not at all or only slightly applicable, but the overall description applies generally to you.

Test Ratings	
Rating & Score	Description
Not very much: 2 points	If one or more parts of the description are not applicable, and if the overall description does not describe you well.
Not at all: 0 points	If the statement does not describe you at all.

The CE-40 Questionnaire

1. I rapidly take charge of a group because I don't like to go unnoticed.

2. I make light of other people's feelings; I am criticized for my lack of sensitivity.

3. I cultivate my inner self; I have a tendency to keep a journal of my intimate thoughts.

4. I am excessively optimistic; I don't overly dramatize life's situations and I have a tendency to act without thinking.

5. People around me get discouraged because of my inertia.

6. I am not preoccupied by my emotions; I'd rather listen to others than discuss my own feelings.

7. I am efficient; I am methodical and regular.

8. I believe in "live and let live" and don't worry much; I love to sleep or do nothing.

9. I want to gain the highest level in my field and am willing to devote the time necessary to achieve it.

10. I am negligent and I believe time will fix everything without my help or intervention.

11. I often feel beaten before I start; I know things will never work out.

12. I am active in all circumstances; I can be the diplomat or the opportunist, and adapt easily to meet the needs of the situation.

13. I am anxious, indecisive, and timid; I often make nervous movements or even bite my fingernails.

14. I am cordial, exuberant, the "life of the party"; I also anger easily.

15. When I am upset or contradicted, I tend to pout and wait for others to guess why; then I want them to console me.

16. I feel the need to embellish reality, to exaggerate the facts; I am told I lack objectivity.

17. I am even-tempered and generally calm.

18. I want to attract attention to myself, even if I have to be seductive.

19. I am objective and fair; I rarely get angry; I don't allow my emotions to interfere with my analysis of a situation.

20. I like to devote time to social and sensual pleasures such as cocktail parties, dinners, cards, games, and lovemaking.

21. I sense I am predestined to participate in noble causes and undertake difficult enterprises.

22. I want to impose my own sense of justice.

23. I need change, excitement, and diversion.

24. I compensate for my vulnerability by clear thinking.

25. I am both optimistic and anxious; I am always in a hurry and afraid of being late.

26. I use cold logic to resolve my problems, considering them one at a time and methodically finding solutions.

27.   I make decisions quickly and on impulse, and I act on them immediately and vigorously.

28.   I am timid, fearful, easily discouraged; I sometimes lack the will to live.

29.   I possess a natural authority and I have the personality of a leader.

30.   I am criticized for undertaking too many things at once; I don't always finish everything I start.

31.   I am demanding of myself and others.

32.   I am criticized for being negligent and lazy.

33.   I am thrifty and cautious; I don't let people take advantage of me.

34.   I am basically accommodating; I don't mind following others.

35.   If I have to criticize someone, I'd rather use humor than harshness.

36.   I guard my solitude and organize my life in advance; I don't like improvised activities.

37.   I like to tease and to play on words, even if it gets a bit heavy.

38.   I am criticized for my changing moods, for my irritability, and even for crying over nothing.

39.   I think people envy me and are jealous of me.

40.   I am often convinced I am right; I like to argue and split hairs to prove a point.

Transfer your scores from the last column of **Grid One** (page 68) onto **Grid Two** (page 69), recording your score for each question in the unshaded column. Total the score for each column. Your dominant character type is represented by the highest score, and your primary tendencies follow in descending order.

	Grid One				
Question	The question describes me				Score
	Very much	Quite a bit	Not very much	Not at all	
1		✓			5
2				✓	0
3		✓			5
4		✓			5
5				✓	0
6			✓		2
7	✓				10
8			✓		2
9	✓				10
10	✓			✓	0
11				✓	0
12	✓				10
13			✓		2
14		✓			5
15				✓	0
16				✓	0
17	✓				10
18			✓		2
19		✓			5
20		✓			5
21			✓		2
22		✓			5
23		✓			5
24		✓			5
25		✓			5
26			✓		2
27		✓			5
28				✓	0
29	✓				10
30	✓				10
31	✓				10
32		✓		✓	0
33		✓	✓		2
34		✓	✓		2
35	✓				10
36				✓	0
37	✓				10
38				✓	0
39			✓		2
40		✓			5

C.E. 40 Quest. Number	Shao Yang Enthusiast	Jue Yin Nervous	Tai Yang Passionate	Shao Yin Sentimental	Yang Ming Metal Phlegmatic	Tai Yin Metal Apathetic	Yang Ming Earth Sanguine	Tai Yin Earth Amorphous
1	5							
2							O	
3				5				
4							5	
5						O		
6								2
7					10			
8								2
9			10					
10		O						
11				O				
12							10	
13		2						
14	5							
15				O				
16		O						
17					10			
18		2						
19					5			
20							5	
21			2					
22						5		
23		5						
24				5				
25	5							
26					2			
27	5							
28				O				
29			10					
30	10							
31			10					
32								O
33						2		
34								2
35					10			
36						O		
37							10	
38		O						
39			2					
40						5		
Total	30	9	34	10	37	12	30	0

Grid Two

Table Three: CE-40 Test Scores			
Character	Score	Character	Score
1. _____	_____	4. _____	_____
2. _____	_____	5. _____	_____
3. _____	_____	6. _____	_____

Determining Your Character Type

The determination of your overall character includes two or three primary character types. In general, the dominant character type receives the highest score on the CE-40 in at least 80% of all tested cases. The next most important tendency receives the second highest score, etc.

In practice, psychology, like medicine and acupuncture, works with the two primary types, more rarely the first three types. You will find that the primary type determined by the results of the CE-40 will match the yin or yang categorization and the constitutional categorization from the hand analysis tests. In other words, if the general characteristics of your hand show a yang tendency, the temperaments that received the highest scores should be predominantly yang. As well, the highest scores for your constitutional types should be for the elements associated with your predominant temperaments. While considering the profile of your temperament and constitution, it may be helpful to review the classical associations of the character types, the six meridians, and the element/organ associations:

Character Type	Temperament	Element & Organ			
Passionate	Tai Yang	Fire	SI	Water	BL
Enthusiastic	Shao Yang	Wood	GB	Fire	TB
Sentimental	Shao Yin	Water	KI	Fire	HT
Nervous	Jue Yin	Wood	LV	Fire	PC
Sanguine	Yang Ming	Earth	ST		
Phlegmatic	Yang Ming	Metal	LI		
Amorphous	Tai Yin	Earth	SP		
Apathetic	Tai Yin	Metal	LU		

Identification of the Dominant Character Type. In a statistical study by Ghislaine Pain (18) of 133 persons, it was shown that 45% of the subjects defined themselves as a single or nearly single character type. The conviction with which they regarded the single description of themselves to be correct was absolute. Likewise, when the subject read to his or her friends a portrait of the character type, such as those in chapter 7, the friends recognized the person without hesitation.

When a singular description adequately describes a person, this is termed a pure character type, a character of a single mold. In general, the behavior is caricatured. The person is almost incapable of behaving in any way other than as he or she is described. This pure character type usually totally follows the character type of the parent the person resembles physically. One says of such a person that he or she is "just like his or her father," or "just like his or her mother." Occasionally both parents have the same dominating character, and have transmitted it to the child.

In the Chinese view the temperament of a person corresponds clearly to the five constitutions. For example, a caricatured enthusiastic, Shao Yang person would be of the wood constitution, or wood and fire. The illnesses are those associated with such a constitution — migraines, allergies, hemorrhoids, liver disease, vertigo, and painful menstruation. A sentimental Shao Yin person would be of water constitution, or water and fire, and the associated illnesses would include hypotension, susceptibility to cold, lumbar pains, and urinary infections. Where a character type is broadly dominant, the corresponding constitution also is broadly dominant, as are the associated vulnerabilities and illnesses.

Identification of the Secondary Character Type. In more than half the cases from the statistical study mentioned above, the subjects stated that two character types were necessary to categorize themselves adequately. Seven percent stated that two types other than the dominant type were necessary for a complete description of themselves. The existence of secondary character types provides a basis for much of the diversity among people, differentiating one passionate type or one sentimental type from another, etc. For example, one individual may be an amorphous passionate type, a second a nervous passionate type. As you read about the temperaments in the following chapters, you will more or less readily discover characteristics beyond the dominant type you recognize as yourself.

The CE-40 takes into account the primary and secondary types, since the eight character types are classified in order of their decreasing scores. In practice it is only the first two or three types that best describe the person, and that are the most important in terms of the terrain and the predisposition to illnesses. Usually there are only two possibilities. The first possibility is that the dominant temperament, although subtlely shaded by secondary temperaments, dominates the person almost exclusively. Generally the score for this character type is considerably higher than the others. Or else, the dominant temperament is followed closely by a corresponding temperament: Shao Yang corresponds to Jue Yin, Tai Yang to Shao Yin, Yang Ming to Tai Yin. In all cases it is the constitutions of these temperaments that dominate the others. Designation of the particular vulnerability is a ready consequence of the determination of the constitutions. For example, if a person has the highest score for enthusiastic and the second highest score for nervous, it is the wood and fire constitutions, respectively, that are designated.

The second possibility is that the primary temperament only slightly dominates the secondary temperament, or there is an equivalence between the two temperaments. In these cases the person has difficulty feeling completely related to either temperament alone. Here the person is defined in all degrees by the collective temperaments. The morphological physique, the tastes, etc., and the vulnerability to specific illnesses are more diffuse.

Such mixing of the temperaments explains why a passionate type can be obese (Tai Yang and Tai Yin-earth), or why an amorphous type can be thin (Tai Yin-earth and Jue Yin). It also explains that a sentimental and apathetic type is thin, since the two temperaments (Shao Yin and Tai Yin) dispose to this, but also that the person can prefer sweets and milk products to salty dishes. Similarly, an enthusiastic and sentimental Shao Yang-Shao Yin can be at the same time optimistic but defeatist, beaten in advance — the eyes radiating a sadness yet a seductive petulance. Persons of a Jue Yin-Tai Yang temperament, nervous and passionate, may be angry with themselves for their instability and seek to overcome their passions by constraint, to give themselves a single goal, refusing to acknowledge a part of their basic character. Likewise an apathetic and enthusiastic Tai Yin-metal and Shao Yang person can get up early and has no difficulty in getting started, and simultaneously evidences a desire to undertake many things; yet is characterized by meticulousness and finds it impossible to act quickly.

There are infinite examples of mixed temperaments. The eight fundamental characters are differentiated by the play of three factors in the yin-yang context (emotive or non-emotive, active or non-active, primary or secondary). It is interesting to note that these character types can be combined to give 64 complex possibilities of human types, just as there are 64 hexagrams possible from the combinations of trigrams according to the *I Ching (Book of Changes)*.

Knowledge of the dominant and secondary character types allows a designation of the corresponding temperaments and vulnerabilities. Complex temperaments necessarily imply overlapping constitutions. The person's specific vulnerabilities can be influenced by different tendencies. For example, based on the scores of the CE-40, consider that a person is categorized as sentimental, nervous, then passionate. This designates the Shao Yin, Jue Yin, and Tai Yang temperaments, and the constitutions water-fire, wood-fire, water-fire. Water appears twice, fire three times, wood once. This person will be very emotive due to fire. Water, appearing twice, will also be important, and wood, although occurring only once, is significant because it occurs in the second highest score. One will therefore find variable signs of disturbance in the functions of these three constitutions.

Compiling the Test Results

Having completed the Analysis of Hand Characteristics, the Evaluation of Childhood Symptoms, and the CE-40, you should have been able to determine, with maximum probability, your primary and secondary constitutions, temperaments, and character types, and thus their likely prevalence in affecting your life, your health, and your behavior. If you are still not quite sure of the test results, the last set of questions, following, will help you to determine your definitive constitutions and their order of dominance. Further reading in the two chapters that follow, "The Five Constitutions" and "The Six Temperaments," in conjunction with review of the different tests, should also help you to make a sure determination.

	Table Four: Compilation of Test Results					
	Your constitutional classification					
Table	*Final Score*	*Wood*	*Fire*	*Earth*	*Metal*	*Water*
1	Hand Analysis					
2	Childhood Symptoms					
3	CE-40 Test					
3	CE-40 Test (1st or 2nd place tied)					
	TOTAL					

Fill out your score from Table 1 (Hand Analysis Results, page 69) on the first line above as follows:

> 7 for your highest hand score
> 4 for your 2nd highest hand score
> 3 for your 3rd highest hand score
> 2 for your 4th highest hand score

Fill out your score from Table 2 (Evaluation of Childhood Symptoms, page 63) on the second line above as follows:

> 7 for the element with the highest score
> 4 for the element with the 2nd highest score
> 3 for the element with the 3rd highest score
> 2 for the element with the 4th highest score

Fill out your score from Table 3 (CE-40 Test Scores, page 70) on the third line above based on your answers to the following guides. Use your first and second highest scores on the CE-40 to determine the scores entered in Table Four. If the first and second temperaments determined by the CE-40 are distinct, leave the fourth line of Table Four (CE-40 #2, page 74) blank. If you have two character types with equal points in either first place, or two character types with equal points in the second place, give the scores to all the elements of your character types, proceeding one by one. That is, if you have a "tie for first" go through the following list answering *as if the first of the tied characteristics were alone in first place.* Then, using the the fourth line provided, record your scores *as if the second temperament were alone in first place.* For example, if you had equal scores for Shao Yang and Jue Yin, complete the following procedure once as if Shao Yang were first and Jue Yin second. Then complete the procedure again as if Jue Yin were first and Shao Yang second. Use this double procedure only if there is a tie for first or second place.

If you are Shao Yang or Jue Yin in the first character, and
　　　　your hand is more normal than long, score 7 in Wood, 3 in Fire
　　　　your hand is more long than normal, score 7 in Fire, 3 in Wood
If you are Shao Yang or Jue Yin in the second character, and
　　　　your hand more normal than long, score 4 in Wood, 3 in Fire
　　　　your hand is more long than normal, score 4 in Fire, 3 in Wood
If you are Tai Yang or Shao Yin in the first character, and
　　　　your hand more short than long, score 7 in Water, 3 in Fire
　　　　your hand is more long than short, score 7 in Fire, 3 in Water
If you are Tai Yang or Shao Yin in the second character, and
　　　　your hand more short than long, score 4 in Water, 3 in Fire
　　　　your hand is more long than short, score 4 in Fire, 3 in Water
If you are Yang Ming or Tai Yin in the first character, and
　　　　your hand more short than long, score 7 in Earth, 3 in Metal
　　　　your hand is more long than short, score 7 in Metal, 3 in Earth
If you are Yang Ming or Tai Yin in the second character, and
　　　　your hand more short than long, score 4 in Earth, 3 in Metal
　　　　your hand is more long than short, score 4 in Metal, 3 in Earth

Now total the scores in Table Four. These totals are a relative, quantitative measure of your constitutional composition. A more visual representation can made by completing the following "bar graph." Shade one of the columns one block for each point scored in Table Four. Do this for each of the five constitutional types in the following empty chart. Once shaded, you can visualize the relative predominance of wood, metal, fire, water, and earth.

Element	Score																									
	.	.	.	.	I	.	.	.	.	I	.	.	.	.	I	.	.	.	.	I	.	.	.	.	.	I
Wood																										
Metal																										
Fire																										
Water																										
Earth																										

Note: each dot equals 1 point, the bars 5 points; if any score is over 25 points, divide all scores by two before plotting.

While it is enjoyable to compare scores with your friends, remember that it is a relative measure. Remember too that if someone has received equal scores for the first or second temperament, their "bars" will be longer than someone with distinct first and second temperaments.

Temperaments are more difficult to visualize because they are a "terrain" or landscape with many features and interrelationships. Also, the qualities of your temperament are more mutable, more subject to changes in the circumstances of your life and personality. To help you confirm and visualize your terrain, complete the following procedure to create another graph that will illustrate the relative emphasis of each temperament.

First write the name and scores for the first, second, and third highest temperaments as determined by your CE-40 test (CE-40 Test Scores, page 70) in Table Five, below:

Table Five — Temperament Summary

Rank	Temperament	CE-40 Score	Yin-Yang	Element	Total
1					
2					
3					

Next, complete the "Yin-Yang" score column according to the following guide. Check each of the three temperaments you have just listed above in the following chart. If your hand was more yin than yang (Test One), use the scores in the "Yin Higher" column, otherwise, use the "Yang Higher" column. If your hand

76

was equally yin and yang in Test One, enter zero in the Yin-Yang columns for all the temperaments listed in Table Five (page 76).

Yin-Yang Scores		
Temperament	Yin Higher	Yang Higher
Tai Yang	0	3
Shao Yang	0	3
Yang Ming Metal	0	3
Yang Ming Earth	0	3
Tai Yin Metal	3	0
Tai Yin Earth	3	0
Shao Yin	3	0
Jue Yin	3	0

To determine your score for the "Element" column of Table Five, use the guide below. Find your three highest element scores from Table Four (page 74). Correlate them with your temperaments listed in Table Five on the guide below. Use the highest scoring element for your highest scoring temperament, noting the score (0,1,2, or 3) where they intersect. Do this for your second highest scoring element and second highest scoring temperament, then your third highest scoring element and third highest scoring temperament. For example, for a highest Jue Yin temperament, with a wood score highest, enter 2 in the "Element" column of Table Five.

Temperament	Element Score				
	Fire	*Earth*	*Metal*	*Water*	*Wood*
Tai Yang	1	0	0	2	0
Shao Yang	2	0	0	0	1
Yang Ming Metal	0	0	3	0	0
Yang Ming Earth	0	3	0	0	0
Tai Yin Metal	0	0	3	0	0
Tai Yin Earth	0	3	0	0	0
Shao Yin	1	0	0	2	0
Jue Yin	1	0	0	0	2

Now, total the scores in Table Five. These totals are a relative measure of the three most descriptive temperaments. The adjustments mildly emphasize the constitutional aspects. A more visual representation can made by completing another "bar graph." Shade one of the columns one block for each point scored in Table Five. Do this for each of the three temperaments you have listed.

Temperament	Rank				
1					
2					
3					

Note: each dot equals 1 point, the bars 5 points; if any score is over 25 points, divide all scores by two before plotting.

To develop a more detailed understanding, read the following two chapters paying particular attention to the constitutions and temperaments emphasized by the tests and summaries in this section. Consider making a list of your most pronounced physical characteristics, habits, and health concerns. Make the lists before you read these chapters and you will be able to keep track of the constitutional and temperamental associations.

The following are good major sections for your list of traits to compare to the information provided in the following chapters:

- Main Physical Complaints
- Main Psychological/Intellectual Concerns
- Physical Habits
- Likes
- Dislikes

Take your time and make a fairly complete list. Physical complaints need not be major problems or diseases, but physical observations you have made frequently. Ask yourself: "If I were perfectly the way I wanted to be, what wouldn't happen any more?" The same idea applies to psychological and intellectual concerns. What kinds of things bother you? Don't forget the positive side. What do you do well, or better than most of your friends? Is there a distinguishing trait or traits that would describe how your mind works? Habits, aren't necessarily "bad habits," but are any regular and routine pattern, for example, going to bed early and getting up early. Likes and dislikes are your preferences, your avoidances.

A knowledge of the various relationships between wood, fire, earth, metal, and water, and their associated organs, provides a complex and adaptable picture of the human system. Combined with an understanding of terrain, it is a powerful tool. However, acupuncturists, physicians, and diathetic physicians all use an array of examination and diagnostic skills. You should not attempt to prescribe any medication, drug or herbal, or use needles and moxibustion without professional guidance. Health professionals seek the advice of their colleagues and rarely treat themselves. Massage, diet, and exercise are deep and worthwhile practices that can be enjoyable and effective for the layperson.

There is a sample case history at the end of chapter 8 that may give you some further ideas about the synthesis of the information related to your character and health.

Chapter 6

The Five Constitutions

The various constitutions are grouped according to the five elements — wood, metal, fire, water, and earth. Each constitution is discussed in the context of the primary characteristics of these elements.

The Wood Constitution

Organ vulnerability. Individuals of wood constitution have a natural weakness of the liver and gallbladder, and their corresponding meridians. The weakness is not necessarily expressed as a strictly hepatic weakness (e.g. digestive symptoms), nor by the symptoms typically associated with gallbladder disease. Because of the influence of intermediary meridians, the symptoms that arise as a result of a weakness of the liver and gallbladder may not be associated with digestion. With proper care and a reasonable lifestyle, symptoms may not arise at all and these vulnerabilities will be expressed as tendencies rather than pathologies.

General morphology. In terms of the overall structure the individual of wood constitution has wide shoulders and good musculature regardless of the overall stature. The complexion is somewhat olive-green, like that of people from the Mediterranean, Provence, Corsica, and Spain. The eyes are large and sometimes protruding; the expression is frank; the eyebrows are wide.

The hand of the person of wood constitution is comparable to the Jupiter hand described by Soulie de Morant.[19] It is muscular with little flesh. The finger joints are like knots of wood, and the nails are hard or even brittle with white points. The nervous wood person will bite their nails. The palm and fingers have numerous, more or less deep streaks. The deeper and more numerous the streaks are, the more assured one can be in making the designation wood for the constitution of this individual. (See the illustration of the Wood hand, page 55, chapter 5).

Childhood symptoms. Various nutritional intolerances are typical in children of wood constitution, including intolerance to chocolate and eggs, and allergic reactions to certain foods (e.g. strawberries). The child generally is boisterous, fearless (although timid at times), nervous, and bites the nails or has tics. Often jaundice is a problem at birth or during childhood.

Adult behavior. Wood subjects are generally fatigued in the morning and have difficulty rising, even if they spontaneously awaken early. They go to bed late and do not get to sleep until late. Intellectually, wood subjects are unstable, with a wavering concentration and a weak memory. Psychologically they are simultaneously optimistic and anxious, nervous, agitated, and can even be aggressive and overly enthusiastic.

Adult illnesses. Common among persons of the wood constitution are allergies to foods, insect bites, the sun, pollens, industrial products, and certain medications. The allergies appear symptomatically as hives, eczema, sometimes asthma, hay fever, or conjunctivitis. Migraines or headaches of the occipital or frontal regions of the head occur, and may be triggered by alcohol, rich meals, annoyances, wind, or menstruation. Digestive problems include symptoms of disturbances in the liver and gallbladder, colitis (predominantly with acute pain occurring on the right side of the body), constipation, and hemorrhoids. Joint pains may occur, and can be acute and fleeting, can change from one joint to another, and generally relate to an increase in the serum level of uric acid. Episodes of tachycardia are also associated with the wood constitution, as well as hypertension, hypotension with sensations of fainting and weakness, vertigo, claustrophobia and fear of empty space, uneasiness in cars, boats, and crowds. Painful menstruation occurs, accompanied by swelling of the breasts, and, more chronically, a tendency to form fibromas in the breast tissue. Excitability with the emaciation typically associated with a disturbance of the thyroid gland can occur in wood subjects. A tendency to goiter and hyperthyroidism is not uncommon. The eyes of wood subjects are sensitive and are subject to viral conjunctivitis, herpes, and myopia. The muscles can be affected by hyperexcitability, with a tendency to frequent spasms.

Likes and dislikes. The wood subject prefers the spring season. It is a season, however, that also is feared, because with the change to spring the person of wood constitution incurs great fatigue or the resurgence of allergies. The wind is feared, for it weakens the body, and gives a feeling of vertigo or headache. The wood person is attracted to acidic or bitter dishes, (e.g., those with vinegar or mustard); or, in contrary fashion, has a strong dislike of these tastes. Salty or sweet tastes are preferred. Dark chocolate is a favorite, and is ingested excessively.

The Metal Constitution

Organ vulnerability. Individuals of metal constitution have a natural weakness of the lungs and large intestine, and their corresponding meridians. The weakness is not necessarily expressed as pulmonary or large intestinal illnesses, but this is frequently the case.

General morphology. The metal individual has a long stature. A slightly bent or hunched posture is often evident, and the breadth of the shoulders is moderate or narrow. The body is thin, the skin white or milky, or, on the contrary, tanned or dull. The nose usually is strong and long.

The hand of the metal individual is long, the palm narrow. The fingers are long and, when closed, make the hand elongated and oval. The fingers do not separate greatly, but they can stretch back easily. The fingers are smooth-surfaced on the front of the hand, and in the joints there is a triple bond. The skin can be dry or rough. The color of the skin is somewhat violet, and turns a cyanotic blue when exposed to the cold. (See the illustration of the Metal hand, page 58, chapter 5).

Childhood symptoms. The child of metal constitution is characterized by thinness, pallor, and lack of appetite. Rhinopharyngitis, bronchitis, or acute laryngitis are common, as is recurring inflammation of the trachea, and an otitis that usually leads to removal of the adenoids. The metal child is predisposed to tuberculosis, but reacts poorly to the BCG vaccine. Measles and whooping cough occur, sometimes severely. Asthma and eczema can occur, with onset at an early age. Constipation and milk intolerance often occur at birth. Later in childhood there may be problems of bedwetting, and, at puberty, undescended testicles, or absence of menstruation. The pliability of the ligaments and growth in rapid spurts predispose the child of metal constitution to scoliosis (deviation of the normal curvature of the spine) and inflammation of the vertebral cartilage.

In terms of attitude, the child of metal constitution is sensible, but grumbling and slow. This slowness and a tendency to distraction usually result in mediocre scholastic achievement during the early years. The metal child needs to go to sleep early, and willingly goes to bed. As an adolescent the child has conflicts with his or her surroundings, and often reacts with mental lassitude.

Adult behavior. Physically the adult individual of metal constitution is easily tired and lacks energy. In the course of the day this person becomes increasingly tired and, by evening, feels exhausted. The person of metal constitution naturally economizes his or her forces and thus acts, speaks, walks, and eats slowly. He or she requires considerable sleep and goes to bed early, and this in turn makes this person an early riser. Frequent periods of rest and vacation are arranged.

Intellectually the metal individual has a certain slowness in the formation of ideas, shows a lack of concentration (resulting occasionally in chronic inattention), and discourages easily. Psychologically this person is calm and inclined more to reflection than outbursts of temper or passion. He or she is of a sad temperament and is generally pessimistic. The melancholic temperament coincides with autumn, the season associated with the metal constitution. Autumn is the season when nature dries and trees lose their leaves. It is also the season that symbolizes the later age of life, a time of reflection and regret for things that have passed.

Adult illnesses. A person of metal constitution suffers from frequent colds, flu, bronchitis, laryngitis, sinusitis, and chronic rhinitis. Asthma is common, and it occurs more frequently in winter when the bronchi are affected. Emphysema is also associated with the metal constitution, as well as tuberculosis, the illness of "sad passions."

Disturbances of the digestive tract appear as chronic colitis. The colon often is enlarged (megacolon). Amoebic infections occur, provoking chronic "alarm-clock" or cock's crow morning diarrhea from 5 a.m. to 7 a.m., waking the subject. Chronic and prolapsed hemorrhoids often necessitate surgical intervention. Symptoms of gastritis can occur.

In acupuncture the lung is associated with the skin and lymphatic system. The metal constitution thus is associated with inflammation of lymph nodes and lymphatic tissue, such as adenitis, which may or may not be pustular. Skin problems are expressed as acne, eczema, psoriasis, mycosis.

Endocrinologically, hypothyroidism is associated with this constitution. This explains in part the susceptibility of the metal person to the cold and their slowness in action and thought. In women there often is insufficient secretion of estrogen and even progesterone, which is opposite to women of wood constitution. This may result in painless menstrual periods, and periods that are long, spaced out, or absent.

There is a lack of tonicity in the ligaments of persons of metal constitution, manifesting as a tendency to frequent spasms, tendonitis, epicondylitis (tennis elbow), shoulder arthritis, and deforming rheumatism. Weakness of the ligaments is associated with frequent twists and sprains.

A tendency to multiple dental caries occurs, as well as recurrent episodes of cystitis due to *E. coli* bacteria.

Likes and dislikes. Metal persons like autumn, although it is this season in which they catch their first colds. The cold travels quickly to the lungs. The cold is felt acutely, and the metal person takes care to wrap the body warmly, especially about the chest and head.

In terms of food, the metal person likes highly seasoned foods. Generally a sweet taste is preferred to salty. Milk and milk products are enjoyed, and are consumed in excess on the pretext of a need for calcium, which in turn is based on a history of rickets in childhood. The metal person also likes chocolate.

The Fire Constitution

Organ vulnerability. Subjects of fire constitution have a natural weakness of the heart and small intestine, and their meridians, or else of the pericardium and triple burner functions. Weakness of these functions does not necessarily result in cardiac crises, nor is the fire constitution the only one subject to such attacks.

General morphology. The complexion of individuals of fire constitution is reddish, either as a result of a ready tendency to blushing, or due to an increased circulation of blood in the face.

The hand is long and the fingers often are longer than the palm, slender and agile. The fingers are capable of spreading far apart, giving the hand the aspect of a sun. The hand is delicate, the nails grow pointed and convex. The pulp of the fingers is frequently quite red. The hand often can be small and thin, in which case, as described in the *Nei Jing,* fire elements are mixed with wood elements. (See the illustration of the Fire hand, page 56, chapter 5).

Childhood symptoms. The symptoms of children of fire constitution are mainly psychological. They are hypersensitive and extremely emotional. Either they are restless, wild, disobedient, stubborn, and frequently liars, or, on the contrary, they are timid, withdrawn, easily influenced, of variable humor, and unstable, alternating between crying and laughing.

When feverish, the temperature of the child of fire constitution often can rise to 104 °F. There is a risk of convulsions, sometimes epilepsy. Physical illnesses are rare.

Adult behavior. The fire subject is inclined to a consuming fatigue that can occur suddenly and be followed by lapses into periods of depression. He or she sleeps only for short periods, requiring only four to six hours a night.

Intellectually the fire personality either enjoys an extraordinary memory accompanied by a sharp intelligence, with a faculty for concentration that is uncommon, or, on the contrary, the memory is defective and unimportant things are retained at the expense of important ones. The intelligence is normal but the concentration remains weak.

Psychologically the behavior of the fire individual may be, from an early age, hypersensitive, hiding his or her emotion, a rebel indignantly fighting for causes against injustice, authoritative, and endowed with a good memory; or he or she may be timid, withdrawn, lacking self-confidence, of variable temper and easily influenced, with a poor memory.

Adult illnesses. The fire constitution is subject to physical problems of a cardiovascular nature, including attacks of hypotension; troubles with the sympathetic nervous system, including spasms of the intestines, stomach, heart, and problems with cardiac rhythm, tachycardia, venous and arterial circulatory problems. Problems with the veins include varices and hemorrhoids; problems with the arteries include angina pectoris, arteriosclerosis, and disturbances in the lower limbs. The fire subject can also suffer from diffuse headaches, from pricking sensations of the scalp and limbs, from spasms such as spastic colon, mainly on the right, and from arthrosis. Metabolically there is difficulty in the elimination of cholesterol, urea, and uric acid.

Likes and dislikes. The fire individual dreads summer and fears heat. He or she may be indifferent to sweet or salty tastes, but savors the bitter flavors such as coffee and tea.

The Water Constitution

Organ vulnerability. Individuals of water constitution have a natural weakness of the kidney, adrenal glands, gonads, or the urinary bladder, and their corresponding meridians.

General morphology. Usually individuals of water constitution have a long stature. When disposed to hyperadrenalism, the water subject will tend to sit or stand erect, the vertebral column straight, the head held high. When disposed to hypoadrenalism, however, the water subject has a tendency to slump, to lower the head and the gaze.

The facial features are incisive, with prominent ridges. The characteristics are typical of the "retracted" model of Corman's morphopsychology (11). The nose of the water individual with hyperadrenalism is like an eagle's beak. The typical complexion of the water individual is dark, like that of Middle Easterners, with a noticeable darkening around the eyes, a signature of persons with renal insufficiency. The eyes tend to be sunken or surrounded by swollen eyelids. (The Chinese refer to these pockets beneath the eyes figuratively as the "room of tears"). The complexion can also be normal or inclined to red, the latter coloration being influenced by an association with the fire constitution.

The hand is spatulate and short, the palm and fingers puffy and soft. One can pinch the skin and separate it easily from the fatty tissue, as if it held excessive water. Classically the hand of the person of water constitution is dark; this is visible on the dorsal surface where the cutaneous folds are abundant. At the level of the joints there is a brown color. The nails are flat and give the ends of the fingers a blunted aspect. The nails have a tendency to curve under, toward the flesh of the fingers. The nail bed has the appearance of a lunar crescent. (See the illustration of the Water hand, page 59, chapter 5).

Childhood symptoms. The child of water constitution is extremely sensitive to the cold and is frequently ill with infectious diseases. Like the child of metal constitution, the child of water constitution is characterized by thinness. But, rather than suffering from respiratory sensitivity, the water individual is primarily vulnerable in the upper respiratory tract. Tonsillitis is common, as well as repeated pustular pharyngeal inflammations that primarily occur in winter. Such inflammations usually lead to removal of the tonsils. If the child does not suffer from pharyngeal inflammations, then he or she commonly suffers from ear infections, often piercing the eardrum. Sometimes both ears are infected, and there are frequent recurrences.

Another characteristic illness associated with the child of water constitution is rheumatic fever, which, when familial, almost certainly verifies the constitutional type of the subject. Other illnesses include impetigo and boils. The presence of albumin in the urine impedes the efficacy of vaccination.

Psychologically the child of water constitution is hypersensitive, secretive, sad and withdrawn. Life for such an individual tends to be one of unhappiness.

As an adolescent the water individual is often delayed in the onset of puberty, and there can be an absence of menstrual periods.

Adult behavior. Physically the adult individual of water constitution is not strong. A sensitivity to the cold is present; the body is frail; and the person often is ill. There is little vitality. Chronic fatigue plagues the hypoadrenal water person, an exhaustion that seems to never leave. If of the hyperadrenal type, the person is conversely exceptionally strong. Intellectually the person of water constitution suffers from poor memory (the hypoadrenal type) or an exceptionally fine memory (the hyperadrenal type). Psychologically, crises of discouragement occur, as well as a disgust with existence, and a disinterest in everything. These crises are accompanied by feelings of profound sadness and a desire to be alone.

Adult illnesses. Urinary disease is common, manifested by frequent episodes of infectious cystitis and other bladder problems, such as a sphincter weakness that causes a frequent need to urinate because retention is difficult. The problems of urinary elimination lead to albuminuria, edema of the eyelids during the morning or of the ankles at the end of the day, and ultimately to kidney or bladder stones. These stones are usually composed of oxalic acid rather than uric acid (wood constitution). Inflammation of the kidney tends to occur during pregnancy. Even in the absence of renal disease these individuals complain of lower back pain. During menstruation the women of water constitution complain of lumbar pain with prolonged sitting or physical exertion.

Other illnesses can be explained by the association of the kidneys with the adrenal glands and gonads, as well as the CNS (including the brain, meninges and spinal cord), the bones and bone marrow (in particular the formation of the red and white blood cells). In the adrenal glands there can be functional or organic insufficiency or an excess of adrenal secretion. From disturbances in the ovaries there can result the cessation of menstruation or pain in the lumbar region that is associated with menstruation. In terms of the skeletal system acute articular rheumatism can occur in childhood. Rickets can occasionally occur in adults, and may be an early indication of a tendency toward rheumatism and, with advanced age, demineralization of bone. Marrow insufficiency appears as deficiencies in the host defense mechanisms, and the subject is susceptible to illnesses of a variety of origins, including viral and bacterial. Acne, boils, staphylococcal and streptococcal infections, and severe shingles occur in these subjects.

The opposition between the kidney and pancreas in the five elements allows us to better understand why the diabetes of a thin person with insulin dependence is a disease primarily affecting the individual of water constitution. The mother-son law in which the kidney-adrenal precedes the liver also explains the appearance of certain forms of jaundice after sudden and great fright. One also can see a degeneration of tissues in the lymphatic system, as well as tumors occurring either in the course of aging or of profound disturbances in the constitution.

A depressed and melancholic state is the natural bias of a person of this constitution, and it is one that, in struggling against it, sometimes leads the person to surpass her- or himself in superior deeds.

Likes and dislikes. The person of water constitution dislikes winter as a result of his or her extreme sensitivity to cold. Cold is felt in the limbs (especially the hands and feet which are icy cold), as well as in the bones and regions of the kidney. In terms of food, a salty taste is preferred to sweet. Salt-cured foods are enjoyed, and there is a tendency to add salt to meals.

The Earth Constitution

Organ vulnerability. Individuals of earth constitution have a natural weakness of the spleen, pancreas, and stomach, and their corresponding meridians, as well as the body fat, joints, collagen, nerve termini, the interstitial fluid, and water metabolism.

General morphology. Earth individuals tend to be of short stature, thick-set, fleshy, often plump or obese. The face is generally broad and round, with large eyes, mouth and nostrils. The lips are thick and the cheeks fleshy. There may be a double chin (11). The complexion is normal or reddish and plethoric. With age these individuals, often called full-blooded or "vascular," are often confused with individuals of the fire constitution. In earth individuals who are hypothyroid, the complexion can be pale and yellowish. In general, the physiognomy and complexion are akin to Asiatics.

The hand is large, wide, and thick. It is in general the hand of an obese person, but varies in degree according to the subject. The palm takes the form of a square, with four equal sides. The fingers are short and pudgy. The nails are triangular (with the tip at the base of the finger), are short, and surrounded by raised tissue on the three borders. (See the illustration of the Earth hand, page 57, chapter 5.)

Childhood symptoms. The baby of earth constitution is large. The child is plump, indeed obese in the pre-pubertal years. This excess weight may or may not diminish after adolescence. The child is gay, carefree and easy to raise. Frequently, however, the child salivates excessively and develops a defect in language skills. The earth child sleeps a great deal and eats a lot, exhibiting a taste for sweets and milk products. Complaints of hiccups and stomachache are frequent. Bedwetting occurs. There is a weakness in the respiratory tract like the child of metal constitution, but perhaps to a lesser degree. Nonetheless, removal of the adenoids is frequent.

The person of earth constitution has a strong prediliction to whooping cough and mumps, and prolonged fatigue in consequence. Viral infections are frequent, as well as intestinal parasites (worms, tapeworms), and fungi (thrush, cutaneous and intestinal mycoses). Like the child of metal constitution, the vision of the child of earth constitution can be farsighted, astigmatic, and exhibit deviation of the eye. Also like the metal child, the earth child risks undescended testes at puberty or absent or irregular menses.

Adult behavior. Physically the adult of earth constitution has a strong constitution. He or she is durable and capable of great stamina, but not always inclined to action. The adult earth individual is lazy, indolent, and neglectful. Fatigue appears in brief but intense episodes when the stomach is empty, at 11 a.m.

91

or 6 p.m. Sudden hunger pangs occur, and concentration is impossible. To alleviate the hunger this person will eat sweets, a light or even a large meal.

Intellectually the earth subject tends to be manipulative and involved in the comparison of ideas. Frequent shortcomings, however, are distraction and forgetfulness, as well as negligence. Psychologically, the earth person tends to have an optimistic view of life. He or she is philosophical and carefree — and yet in some individuals these tendencies are sometimes carried into a severe melancholy or an alternation between these two contrary moods.

Adult illnesses. There is a tendency to excess eating and good living. Gastric pains, gastritis, stomach ulcers, pancreatitis, hiatal hernias, diabetes, obesity, and a tendency to form cellulite are constitutional vulnerabilities for earth subjects. They may also suffer from colitis on the right side, diarrhea, and constipation; fungal infections of the cheek, digestive tract, or skin; chronic bronchitis, asthma, hypertension, cardiac problems, arteritis, early prostatitis, troubles with ovulation, irregular menstruation with weight gain from cycle to cycle, frigidity, premature ejaculation, hypothyroidism, rheumatism (arthrosis), eczema, psoriasis, premature baldness, considerable dental decay, sinusitis, candidiasis of the mucous membranes of the cheek, excessive secretion of saliva, and premature cataract.

Likes and dislikes. The earth subject dreads heat almost as much as humidity. There is generally only a slight sensitivity to cold, except in the presence of hypothyroidism, which is a special case. The heat travels to the cheeks, making them flushed, which in turn makes the person perspire and become sleepy, especially after meals. Humidity aggravates the rheumatism, the asthma, the chronic bronchitis, and the sinusitis.

The earth subject prefers a sweet taste. A meal never ends without a sweet or a pastry. Earth individuals sweeten their coffee more than others. There is a fondness for dishes with sauces, old-style cooking. "Live to eat and not eat to live" would be the motto of an earth subject.

Chapter 7

The Six Temperaments

"The wise doctor knows the temperament of the patient." — J.J. Rousseau

The Shao Yang Temperament

Constitution. Shao Yang is the name given to the meridians of the gallbladder and the triple burner. The Shao Yang person is of wood constitution, vulnerable in the gallbladder function more than the liver, or else of wood and fire constitution, and vulnerable in the elimination function of the triple burner.

General behavior. The general demeanor of the Shao Yang person is martial. The temperament is warm, spirited, volcanic, "fiery." The eyes, under the command of the element wood, are often wide, large, with open brow ridges. The look is warm, sparkling, but also penetrating. From the relationship of the gallbladder with vision (vitamin A) the Shao Yang person generally has excellent visual acuity. The face is open and frank, completely like the individual.

The complexion is normal, well colored, or else greenish, olive, or bronzed like that of the Latin people along the Mediterranean border. When the person has a gallbladder disease, this coloring can become ashen and grey.

Shao Yang persons are of all sizes and shapes, but generally they are not large although they are well built. The model appearance is that of the sharp and lively Mediterranean. The extreme tonicity of the muscular system is associated with facial tics, of which the most frequent is contraction of the jaws (trismus) or a spasming of the eyelid that jerks the eye.

The Shao Yang person is often a sports devotee who practices several physical activities; he or she loves competition and fearlessly takes risks. The body usually is nimble and agile, although there often is some limitation of movement, usually of the rotation and lateral bending of the trunk.

The person of Shao Yang type is active, never staying still. Both body and mind are impatient. He or she is always going or coming. Wherever possible, the Shao Yang individual tries to be noticed.

In terms of sleeping, the Shao Yang type prefers going to bed late and sleeping late. In the morning, however, even if the person is a morning person, there is some difficulty waking up, and a long time is required before the person feels completely awake and can get going.

The Shao Yang individual is not susceptible to the cold. The wind or heat is dreaded.

In childhood, the Shao Yang type is rarely sick. Although thin, he or she is solid. Some attacks of the liver occur, with vomiting or migraines.

Intellectual behavior. In youth, the Shao Yang person enjoys a good memory, although, with age, this can undergo a sudden alteration. Intellectually this individual is full of ideas and imagination. He or she has a disorderly intelligence, a wild, even blundering creativity, and a strong or grandiloquent inspiration.

Psychological behavior. The Shao Yang temperament corresponds to the enthusiastic type of Berger. This person is emotive, active, and primary. He or she acts and reacts immediately, "without thinking," by impulse or intuition. They are optimistic, combative, and anxious all at once. He or she is full of projects, excited about many things simultaneously. But the activity is disorderly and is not always sustained. If many projects are undertaken few materialize. To this person can be applied the formula "grab all, lose all." Although these persons might well characterize themselves as passionate, in characterology passionate persons are those for whom a single passion is followed to its end.

The Shao Yang person is cordial, entering easily into relationships with others, though sometimes in a too rapidly familiar way. This type is the proverbial merrymaker in company, and the more so because he or she is endowed with a facility for speaking, even in public. But moderation is generally lacking, and impetuosity usually makes this person commit errors of taste. In characterology such attitudes are designated exuberant or enthusiastic, considered synonymous with choleric.

The bellicose nature of this temperament is manifested early. The youth is intrepid, the leader of the pack. As an adult he or she gets carried away over nothing. The anger can be blinding, and sometimes leads to senseless and violent acts, such as breaking objects, throwing dishes. Yet the anger passes as quickly as it arises. It is a sudden, short blaze, and when it ends the outrage will be regretted. Since the Shao Yang type also is generous, one says that they wear their hearts on their sleeves but are not spiteful. Emotive, sensitive, and generous, the Shao Yang person does not like to do ill to others, and they defend their frequent outbursts of temper as excesses of honesty. Shao Yang individuals like to say what is in their heart, and they cannot keep reproaches to themselves that perhaps should not be spoken, because they cannot cheat or compromise. Their anger and lack of tact, therefore, are often, in their eyes, the proof of their frankness.

However, Shao Yang persons are not always angry or violent. Some do not explode, but keep their aggressivity inside. The most common trait is an absence of spite. They say what has to be said, and that is all. No more is spoken about it.

The feverish activity of the Shao Yang type, who always is in a hurry, as though there is not enough time to do all that must be done, is accompanied by anxiety. An awareness of life as a brief period makes this type of person arrive early to an engagement, and, once there, await the exact time impatiently. The anxiety can become an agony, an agitation over nothing, even though it may contradict their innate optimism.

In difficult situations the Shao Yang person is stimulated because he or she likes to fight and face conflict directly. Shao Yang types are primarily prompted to act by their taste for action and anxiety, which compel them to move. They cannot stay still and do nothing, without being angered, inhibited, bored. They throw themselves headlong into their work, which for them is a salvation and a continual source of enjoyment.

The Shao Yang person seeks pleasure in all the activities of life, including sports, or love — where a number of affairs can be going on at the same time. This the Shao Yang person describes as a "conservative infidelity" (3). Conflicts do not disturb the Shao Yang. They react strongly, and enjoy the opportunity to feel their force and to manifest their power.

The Shao Yang person does not accept being ill, and does not like to be taken care of. He or she puts confidence in nature and always puts off seeking professional advice. When treatment is accepted — taking some rest, for example, or following some special diet for a while (which is rare because the Shao Yang is so undisciplined), recovery is rapid and the person returns to living life intensely. Shao Yang are leaders. For them, action is uppermost.

Correspondence in the arts and history. One can cite historical personalities, writers, and artists, whose particular character or that of their works suggests the Shao Yang type. Victor Hugo is a good example. He was socially active, a politician and a writer; he had a wife, a big family, and numerous extramarital affairs. "Fights are always good," he writes in the preface to *The Orientals.* In music one can cite the works of Beethoven and the style of military music. Cinema personalities might include Jane Fonda, who shows a combination of Shao Yang and Tai Yang traits, or John Wayne — Shao Yang epitomized in the cowboy mythology. Ronald Reagan exhibits many Shao Yang traits.

Correspondence in ethnic groups and nationalities. The Shao Yang type corresponds to the Iberian peoples and to peoples along the coast of the Mediterranean (Spaniards, Portuguese, Corsicans, Sicilians, and Provencals, among others) whose folklore (the exuberant music and dances) suggest Shao Yang. Among the Asian countries, the Japanese could be considered Shao Yang.

It is interesting to note in Berger's work the attempt to describe dominant character types for nationalities. The hypothesis that a temperament and a morbidity impregnates the individuals of a race or ethnic group demands prudence in application and cannot be applied absolutely. However, it does warrant consideration as a potential basis for studies in comparative epidemiology.

The Jue Yin Temperament

Constitution. Jue Yin is the name given to the meridians of the liver and pericardium. The Jue Yin person is of wood constitution, vulnerable in the liver, or else of wood and fire constitution, vulnerable in the orthosympathetic function of the pericardium. The person of this temperament is mobile, variable, and as fleeting as the wind. According to Berger, the Jue Yin person is emotive, non-active, and primary.

General behavior. The general demeanor of the Jue Yin person is might be characterized as nervous. He or she can be inhibited and timid or, on the contrary, excited and animated, emotionally expressive, and hypersensitive. The inhibited Jue Yin type hides and does not dare move, bites the nails and lips, can have tics, constantly fusses with the hair, clenches the hands, and twists the fingers. The animated Jue Yin type is mobile, agitated, and talks constantly. Often the Jue Yin woman, more than the man, rapidly licks the lips in a nervous and seductive way. The active Jue Yin is superficially akin to the Shao Yang in other ways as well, but active Jue Yin persons merely pretend or imagine themselves to be active.

The Jue Yin complexion is also variable. It can be pale and dull, and even more pale when the person is under emotional strain. Beads of perspiration can appear over the forehead and give the impression of imminent fainting — which is sometimes the case. Alternatively, the complexion can be rosy. During emotional stress it may become red from the feet to the head. The face is then noticeably red and the skin is flushed from congestion of the capillaries.

97

The physical description, demeanor, attitudes, and complexion of these two profiles reflect the dominant constitutions. The pale, timid, inhibited person has a constitution where wood dominates fire; the red, chattering, agitated person has a fire constitution dominating wood.

The Jue Yin subject is often myopic, after the trait of either parent, or from a time when he or she suffered an illness of the liver, like jaundice. The eyes of the Jue Yin type are often beautifully expressive and fascinating — wide-open, gazing near and far simultaneously, imparting a mysterious air and a strange charm. The look may also reflect the inner emotions of the person; fatigue can dull this normal brightness.

The Jue Yin type fears the wind, which "turns the head" and creates sensations of vertigo and confusion. This feeling can also arise in empty spaces, in an airplane or boat, in a car, or in the middle of a crowd. Spring is the favorite season, but here again, especially at the start, it can create a sense of vertigo or great fatigue.

In childhood the Jue Yin person is generally in good health, but thin. Liver attacks can occur, such as jaundice at birth or, later, a viral hepatitis. Ketonemia (often a flag for diabetes) is specific to this temperament.

Intellectual behavior. The Jue Yin person corresponds to the nervous type described by Berger. This person has problems of recall; often it is the emotions that cause the lack of memory. The imagination is lively and the artistic quality of the inspiration makes this person an aesthete in art, literature, film, and the theater.

Psychological behavior. Great variability in mood is characteristic of the Jue Yin, as well as anxiety, with escape into dreams and distraction. Emotivity and variability of mood give this person the appearance of being neurotic. Moments of intellectual or affective excitation alternate suddenly and frequently without apparent reason with moments of discouragement and outbreaks of tears. In the Jue Yin woman this mood is dependent on menstrual cycles, which render her irritable and depressed. Intolerance to the birth control pill is typical, and induces the same moods that are associated with her periods.

The instability of mood is linked to instability of character. The Jue Yin person works in an irregular fashion, and only at what he or she finds pleasing. There is sometimes a morbid lack of self-confidence. This lack makes the person feel conflicts to an extreme degree. The two reactions are, however, variably mixed in this type, and are proportional to the dominant constitution.

The first mode of reaction in the Jue Yin type is inhibition and anguish, the second is flight. Inhibition, anguish, and fear are often linked by the principles of acupuncture to a liver weakness.

Constantly on the alert, the Jue Yin person is permanently agitated and distressed about everything and nothing. The anxiety provokes inhibition and uneasiness, both over the person and the problem. Paralyzed by stage fright, they dread speaking in public. Even the most banal activities, like driving, walking in the street, or running errands can be a source of great distress. Inhibition creates a state of tension, and often this tension passes unnoticed by others. Thus, the sudden emotional storms that appear for no apparent reason come as a surprise, and the outbreaks of tears are as strong and as spectacular as they are brief.

Because the Jue Yin person is not fundamentally sad but, on the contrary, is optimistic, he or she often is capable of surmounting perceived handicaps. Frivolity and escape serve this purpose well, although superficially. Escape takes the form of the most varied diversions, performances, games, but also a taste for intellectual stimulation and imagination. This might manifest as participation in several amorous liasons or ingestion of artificial excitants like coffee, tobacco, or alcohol, although many Jue Yin subjects do not tolerate alcohol well. Its use may produce vertigo, migraines or nausea. The objective of these diversions is to forget the weight of the problems that are a constant plague.

The quest for diversions that is characteristic of the Jue Yin type, and the tasting of all the pleasures of life that is characteristic of the Shao Yang type, can be explained by an understanding of Taoist precepts. In a classical Chinese medical text, the *Nei Jing,* it is stated, "The three months of spring evoke an unfolding. The universe is lying in childbirth; creation is in its bursting stage. One goes to bed late and gets up early; one leaves the house, loosens the hair, becomes at ease and tastes life."

These two temperaments are of wood constitution and thus conform to the natural laws of the seasons, to the "Tao of spring-time," as the ancient Chinese said. But fire, to which belong the meridian and function of the triple burner and pericardium, also links these temperaments to summer. One seeks the sun, puts oneself in a good mood, and brightens up such that the energy of the interior of the body can be exteriorized of its own accord. The corresponding Tao is to "cultivate growth; to run counter to this wounds the heart" (20).

The escape pattern of the Jue Yin person can be expressed symbolically. With the exceptional imagination that is characteristic of this person, he or she is transported into regions where nothing can pursue or reach them. Jue Yin persons thus turn their back on objectivity and surround themselves with the idealized values of the dream world. They turn to artistic creations, poetry mainly, or the theater, and come to believe in the dream that they have created. It is a belief that makes their life resemble a fable. This is their refuge. The person that has been formed in their soul is their mask, consciously or unconsciously created to provide a change.

They constantly feel the need to embellish this image, to mystify their person in the eyes of others. There is thus a need to surprise and attract the attention of others. This need may even include seduction. Seduction is of course the need to attract the interest of the opposite sex, or of everyone, to oneself.

Simulation of a free and easy air is also possible, feigning an attitude that is totally relaxed, or feigning a symptom more or less consciously to attract attention. Such feigning is all the more easily spontaneously produced in the Jue Yin type because the sympathetic nervous system in these individuals is already constitutionally liable and hyperexcitable.

The seesawing between inhibition and compensation that characterizes Jue Yin persons may appears now as timidity, anxiety and inhibition, and later as loquaciousness, exhibitionism, a falsely relaxed manner, and constant chatter, inundating themselves and others with an uninterrupted flood of words.

In terms of health, Jue Yin individuals suffer from various troubles that, though disturbing or annoying, are not serious. They often consult physicians, going from one to the another, and do not follow for long the advice and prescriptions recommended.

Correspondence in the arts and history. Many Jue Yin persons of rich imagination have acquired recognition in the arts. This is especially true in poetry, and examples of such persons are Baudelaire and Edgar Allen Poe. In films, one can cite James Dean and Woody Allen; or Marilyn Monroe and the completely Jue Yin myth that has surrounded her.

Correspondence in ethnic groups and nationalities. The French character seems to correspond to the nervous Jue Yin. This would be fitting, given the reputation of the French in the arts, cuisine, and fashion — the dilettante and aesthetic expressions of the French culture. It would also explain the frailty of the liver that is thought by so many French people to be their major malady. The Italian character also seems to be Jue Yin, but more fire than wood, more pericardium than liver.

The Tai Yang Temperament

Constitution. Tai Yang is the name of the yin-yang tandem formed by the meridians of the small intestine and bladder. The Tai Yang person is most often of water or fire constitution. Fire is rarely present without water in this temperament, which is why, even if the person is inflamed by passion, there is an attitude of coldness, distance, and authority. This trait depends on an excess of the yang bladder meridian, of the water constitution.

The bladder meridian is linked not only to its function as a reservoir for urine. In its course along the vertebral column to the brain it has a role in the activity of the CNS. There is a direct relationship between an excess of this function and a hyperexcitability of the CNS. Symptoms of bladder meridian excess are: psychosis, epilepsy, convulsions, meningitis that causes the spinal column to bend in a backward arc.

The fire constitution has a vulnerability of the small intestine and its meridian, which, by a direct coupling with the heart, explains the hyperemotivity and hypersensitivity of this temperament.

In childhood this type of person can suffer from nosebleeds, epilepsy, or convulsions as a result of fever. The Tai Yang child has a hyperexcitable nervous system, particularly if their birth was difficult.

General behavior. The general bearing of the Tai Yang person is rigid. The body is held erect. The figure is slender. The muscles are long spindles endowed with a strength that is more nervous than muscular. This posture holds the mark of a certain nobility. The head is held noticeably straight, almost bent backward, and there is little flexibility. The person is obliged to turn their entire body to look to the right or left. All this confers on their silhouette a slender and proud magnificence.

This erect and arched attitude reveals an excess of the bladder meridian. There is also excess energy in the small intestine meridian. It is this meridian that is needled for stiff neck, to which the Tai Yang person is often victim.

This carriage of the head, its elegance, its thoroughbred air, makes Tai Yang persons appear to have a high opinion of themselves. They stare down their audience with an air of superiority. They collect their gestures and words into a dignified form, which adds to their natural elegance, and gives the impression that they scorn all those who are not like them.

The complexion of the Tai Yang person is generally unremarkable. With age and atherosclerosis the facial skin becomes a deep brick-red or darker, especially around the eyes. The look is often hard and cutting, dominating or condescending. One rarely perceives it as hypersensitivity or generosity.

Though the Tai Yang person likes sports and will try to be first in competition, the Tai Yang body is not overly supple; there is difficulty in bending both physically and mentally. Severe lumbar pains and paralyzing sciatica are common. The Tai Yang person dreads heat as well as cold, sometimes one or the other, sometimes both at once. Generally winter is not enjoyed, even if the individual is not susceptible to the cold.

Intellectual behavior. Tai Yang persons remember their emotional past well, the wrongs that were inflicted on them, and the victories that were gained. Their intellectual memory is also excellent. They possess a considerable faculty for learning and retention, an enormous capacity for work, and an often superior intelligence. Sleep, however, may often be brief and restless, and this pattern continues from youth onward.

Psychological behavior. The Tai Yang temperament corresponds to the passionate type of Berger, emotive, active, and secondary. In acupuncture Tai Yang is the greatest yang. For Berger, this character type possess the greatest propensities. This person is the "ambitious person who realizes goals." The activity of Tai Yang individuals is directed toward a single, lofty goal, or, in other words, a single passion. It is not that they try to bring everything before them, in anarchic fashion. On the contrary, they try to subordinate to their single chosen ambition anything that might deter them. Where Shao Yang individuals live their passions wildly, giving themselves to the free play of their fantasies, Tai Yang individuals hold themselves in check and prevent any interference with their chosen course. Tai Yang persons create a disciplinary system that subordinates everything to their passion. The work undertaken, to which they are prepared to dedicate themselves life-long, is one for which they will sacrifice everything to achieve perfect realization.

The egotistical concerns of the Tai Yang type are considerable, because, as Berger says of the passionate type, "this person suffers as a result of all that he or she has neglected, and pays with his or her happiness for the success of this or that enterprise" (3).

The passion of Tai Yang persons is expressed frequently as an enthusiasm for art, a style, an author, an ideology. Proud and jealous of their choices, in which they become totally immersed, they speak of their causes hotly and only tolerate contrary argument with difficulty. They harbor a certain scorn for those who do not share their tastes and ideals.

The self-sacrificing quality of their pursuits often leads Tai Yang individuals to adapt a most austere lifestyle. This is not always expressed in an absolute fashion, but it is the major tendency to which all Tai Yang persons aspire.

The Tai Yang child is difficult to raise. The character is difficult, rebellious, stubborn, and in perpetual opposition to authority. He or she is at once vulnerable and rebellious, learning progressively to master and utilize his or her violence, hiding the emotivity and great sensitivity. Because temperaments are hereditary, it is rare that the Tai Yang child does not have a Tai Yang mother or father. The Tai Yang parent is authoritarian, sober emotionally, and constraining. It is only natural that such a child comes into early and dramatic conflicts with parental authority. These conflicts carry over as a difficulty entering into other relationships. The Tai Yang person often feels misunderstood, rejected and persecuted.

Naturally authoritative, the Tai Yang person is possessive and suffers from a sharp, excessive, and unhealthy jealousy. The opposition to the brutish behavior that is provoked in others sometimes leads the Tai Yang person to isolation or exile. A weakness of this temperament is that Tai Yang individuals seldom recognize their wrongs. Usually they deny them vehemently, even dishonestly. Sometimes they deny them simply because they do not recognize them. By contrast they possess qualities of generosity, devotion, an honorable and willing spirit, and incorruptible integrity. Berger (3) observed that such persons take their country, family, and religion seriously. A characteristic tendency of this type of individual is the will to be best in everything, at the price of any effort.

In terms of their relationship with their physician, it must be a privileged one; if not, they mistrust and change quickly to another. When the relationship is successful, they conform scrupulously to whatever advice the physician may give.

Correspondence in the arts and history. In the cosmos, Tai Yang, or Great Yang, is the sun. Among Tai Yang personalities are the great figures of history: Alexander the Great, Caesar (who was epileptic), Michelangelo (according to Berger), Catherine the Great of Russia, Napoleon, Marie Curie, General De Gaulle. Current figures might include Margaret Thatcher, Mohamar Qaddafi, Ayatollah Khomeini. In the arts, one can cite the music of Wagner and Mahler, and the literature of Dostoyevsky. In cinema, Tai Yang figures would include Orson Welles, Ursula Andress, and Barbara Streisand.

Correspondence in ethnic groups and nationalities. Slavic culture seems to be closely associated with the Tai Yang temperament, having a sense of grandeur, a passionate character, and a conquering air, yet transformed at once into sentimental beings by the music of gypsy violins.

The Shao Yin Temperament

Constitution. Shao Yin is the name given to the meridians of the kidney and heart. The Shao Yin person is of water constitution, vulnerable in the kidney-adrenal-gonad function, or of water and fire constitution, vulnerable in the heart and circulatory functions. A person of this temperament is withdrawn, introverted.

General behavior. The general demeanor of the Shao Yin person is one of introversion and timidity. There is a tendency to bow the head and lower the eyes. The person acts briskly, with quick and rapid movements, and can be awkward, which increases their timidity.

The Shao Yin person is supple, but somewhat limited in the ability to draw the body upward by throwing the chest forward. A chronic lumbar pain is usually present. This person is not an amateur devotee of sports.

The facial complexion is red, not like that of a plethoric person, but in a more discrete fashion, localized almost uniquely to the cheeks, but without being blotchy. Over the basic coloring the person frequently reddens, like the Jue Yin person, as a result of timidity. The complexion can, however, become dark, like that of Middle Easterners, with deterioration of the kidney function or with advancing age, particularly around the eyes.

The eyes usually have dark circles around them, and when they are swollen, mainly in the lower eyelids in the morning, it indicates poor elimination by the kidney or the triple burner. (This appearance also can be seen in the Shao Yang person and, in general, in all persons with age when elimination is poor.)

The Shao Yin look is moving and pathetic, for the eyes are almost always teary, like that of a deeply distraught person. Yet there is in the eyes a reflective quality, evoking a picture of the reflection of the moon on the surface of water, which is opposed to the flamboyant and solar look of the Shao Yang person. The pathetic tendency gives Shao Yin individuals an apparent air of coldness because their hypersensitivity usually makes them overly cautious. Shao Yin persons want to give a relationship their complete trust and reveal their sensitivity of heart. At the same time they wish to draw away if there is the slightest possibility of suffering from such an exposure of themselves. Thus Shao Yin individuals, without being arrogant, deceitful, or dominating, give all or none of their trust, because it hinges so much on their heart.

Sometimes the border of the eyes is red like that of a person who has cried a lot. Sometimes the look is dull, lusterless and ashen. In the lowering of the eyes there is a fear to bear another person's gaze for a long time, or else the look is oblique, suggesting hidden motives.

Shao Yin individuals are very susceptible to cold. They hate winter, which gives them the feeling of shriveling up. The sensitivity and behavior can be compared to the description of the seasons in the *Nei Jing:* "The three months of winter evoke reclusion. Water freezes. One goes to bed early, arises late, not before daylight. One acts as though hibernating, fleeing the cold, seeking warmth." The corresponding Tao is "to live as a recluse" (20). This Tao applies perfectly to the Shao Yin, both figuratively and literally. It also applies in part to certain Tai Yang individuals of water constitution.

In childhood the Shao Yin person is generally frail and can suffer from frequent otitis or tonsillitis, infections, impetigo, or boils. Acute articular rheumatism is somewhat specific to this temperament.

Intellectual behavior. Shao Yin persons remember their past well and are extremely attached to it; this is their emotional memory. By contrast, the intellectual memory is faltering. Memorization is difficult. The intelligence is usually more conceptual than practical.

Shao Yin persons are opinionated. They do not like to act; action is costly. But they are conscientious and scrupulous, and this is sometimes their only impetus for pursuing a particular endeavor.

106

Psychological behavior. The Shao Yin person corresponds to the sentimental character type of Berger, emotive, non-active, and secondary. "This is the ambitious person who aspires rather than produces. Awkward, such persons resign themselves to what could in fact be avoided." But, preferring this not to be known, they will persist in their efforts. In their successes they are modest and full of humility. Yet, expecting failure, they are not surprised when it happens. The sentimental type, according to Berger, is also analytical; such persons "know exactly their weaknesses and try to transform their character." Shao Yin individuals are melancholic and dissatisfied with themselves and their lives. They reproach themselves over and over, and accept neither their weaknesses nor their vulnerability. The more they fail the more they reproach themselves.

Being timid, Shao Yin individuals do not know how to enter into relationships. They complain of their lot, and continually reassess the negative elements in their past and imagine what might have been. They thus suffer from discouragement, from feeling the absurdity of existence, of the futility of effort, of despair in humanity, and sometimes from the desire to live no longer.

The childhood of the Shao Yin person is one of sadness. The child is "orphaned," misunderstood, and hurt because of his or her extreme sensitivity. The sensitivity leads to envy and a tendency to misanthropy. In the *Nei Jing* it is said, "The Shao Yin person is envious, rejoicing in the misfortune of others, and always has an air of coldness. In walking the head is always lowered." Pleasure over the misfortune of others gives rise to considerable self-blame. Compensation can often come as opposing and sublimated feelings of devotion and self-sacrifice. Envy and the feeling of inferiority push this individual into using great cunning when dealing with people, particularly in business. These are qualities reputed to be connected with the *zhi,* the vegetative spirit of the kidney, of water.

Shao Yin adolescents possess a natural penchant for introspection and analysis, which often prompts them to keep an intimate journal — which they usually keep hidden. They know exactly their own weaknesses and attempt to transform their character. Shao Yin individuals like to practice meditation, which they believe offers the possibility of compensating for their failures by inaction in the ideal. Their profoundly felt sadness is proof of their greatness. Lucidity of mind is a quality to which they most often cling.

Shao Yin individuals often express their ideal in love. While still young they cultivate the romantic ideal of absolute love. All their lives they carry this ideal within themselves. Monogamous and faithful, they demand this perfection of their passion, and impose the same demands on their partner. As such they are fiercely jealous, and become extremely upset by infidelity — either their own or their partner's. Shao Yin individuals are often bound to their first love; it is difficult to give themselves twice.

Because Shao Yin persons are determined most by their hypersensitivity, they can evolve in various ways. Either they abandon themselves to a destiny of sadness, satisfying masochistically their penchant for blackness, and complain ceaselessly, or they may force themselves, with self-control and analysis, to endure their misfortune. In this quest they find a closeness to nature, in which they often isolate themselves so that they may recharge. In this contact with nature, incursive reflection supplies these individuals with the strength to endure their sorrows, or at least to let nothing of their vulnerability become visible. They are therefore free to cultivate a certain interior detachment and severity.

Intimate exchange in love and friendship greatly affects the way they feel. Their nature is not so much pessimistic as defeatist, but if affective equilibrium can be achieved, they become optimists.

Through a constitutional vulnerability Shao Yin persons can be attacked by severe infections or illnesses that can become chronic. They know this; they feel it. This is why they take precautions and pay attention to their health. They consult physicians readily and docilely follow medical advice.

Correspondence in the arts and history. In literature there are many sentimental Shao Yin types. A famous example would be Jean-Jacques Rousseau's intimate journal, "The Confessions." In this journal the author describes his love of nature. Stendhal, whose most famous novel, *The Red and the Black*, contains in its title the symbolic colors of fire and water, exhibits the characteristics of this temperament. The personalities of Einstein and Gandhi also are representative. In film the figure of Charlot, created by Charlie Chaplin, incarnates with comic derision the Shao Yin tendency to tears, failure, bungling timidity and sentimentality. In music, the andante and adagio movements often typify the Shao Yin temperament. Examples include the adagio of Albinoni, the andante from the Concerto d'Aranjuez, and the quality of the Second Piano Concerto of Rachmaninoff. African American spirituals and the blues also typify this temperament.

Correspondence in ethnic groups and nationalities. The most characteristic Shao Yin ethnic group seems to be Middle Easterners, Jews and Arabs. Their folklore and music are filled with plaintive tones and sentimentalism. African races also exhibit facets of the Shao Yin temperament.

The Yang Ming Temperament

Constitution. Yang Ming is the name given to the meridians of the large intestine and stomach. The Yang Ming person is of earth constitution, vulnerable in the stomach function, or of metal constitution, vulnerable in the large intestine function, or both at the same time. The temperament is extroverted and optimistic.

If the dominating constitution is earth, it is of the primary type and the character is sanguine. The vulnerabilities are mainly digestive (stomach and pancreas) and circulatory.

If the dominating constitution is metal, it is of the secondary type and the character is phlegmatic. This person is less extroverted than the Yang Ming person with earth as the dominating constitution. The vulnerability is mainly digestive (colon) and respiratory (the large intestine is linked to the lung), and circulatory. The connection of the stomach and large intestine with the arterial circulation has already been discussed. There is a direct relationship in the course of these two Yang Ming meridians to the blood vessels. The paths are superimposable on the course of the large arteries. This relationship explains further the basis of the sanguine character.

109

In practice the two types (sanguine and phlegmatic) are often mixed in persons of Yang Ming temperament, but one can encounter more or less pure sanguine and pure phlegmatic, or clear cases of one dominating the other. It is therefore useful to analyze the two types separately as Yang Ming-earth, the character type corresponding to sanguine, and Yang Ming-metal, the phlegmatic type.

Yang Ming-earth

General behavior. As the name indicates, it is the earth constitution that dominates. The general demeanor is steady, centered. Of thick and bony frame, this person has broad shoulders and hips, a short neck. The body is not supple and is slow to react, but powerful. If sports are practiced it is for pleasure or for maintaining the figure — which is lost immediately when the practice is ceased. This person therefore works out with the greatest regularity.

The face is round, open, affable, jovial, welcoming. The lips are often fleshy and full. The complexion is frankly red, even apoplectic. Blotchiness can settle in at an early age, or there will be a clear redness at the tip of the nose, the earlobes, or the whole ear, indicating from youth the vascular aspect of the temperament. The expression is mild, the eyes a bit globular like doe or oxen, joyous, laughing, or even malicious. But at the same time the expression radiates benevolence, a reassuring and paternal energy. With age the Yang Ming-earth person becomes bald in the forehead and at the top of the head.

There is a tendency in this constitution to overheating of the yang of the stomach. Such persons dread not only humidity but also heat, which overwhelms them or leaves them sleepy. They thus dread the summer. In terms of foods, these individuals like everything, from dishes with sauces to desserts. Sweets are a favorite. They do not always salt their food, but willingly sweeten their desserts and coffee.

In childhood Yang Ming-earth individuals are generally in good health. They are usually plump or even obese, and manifest from birth a large appetite and marked attraction to sweets. There may be episodes of winter nasopharyngitis, bronchitis or sinusitis, with a concomitant thinness. These episodes taper off as the child grows older, stronger and larger. This trend is an expression of the subjacent metal constitution.

Intellectual behavior. Yang Ming-earth persons have a good memory. They use mnemonic devices effectively. They like the play of words, the association of ideas and sonorities, and puns. They like songs with refrains, proverbs, popular sayings, farce, gallant stories, and lecheries.

Psychological Behavior. The Yang Ming-earth type corresponds to the non-emotive type; this is the first of the four non-emotive character types to be studied. The person also is active and primary, corresponding to the sanguine character described by Berger.

Yang Ming-earth persons are extroverts who dedramatize everything by the absence of emotivity. Their conflicts are lived as a game. With their hyperactivity and dynamism they take pleasure in vanquishing obstacles. They are inclined to be objective, have their feet on the ground, and exercise good practical sense. Their sense of practicality moves them to find ingenious solutions to problems.

Extroverted, they like human contact more than anything else, meeting with friends, joining clubs for fishing and hunting. They will play their favorite games and at the same time tell story after story. They are the life of the party. But they are also courteous and worldly (3), and enjoy the rules of good society where their sense of irony and spiritual skepticism bring them great success. They have qualities of diplomacy, and they are endowed with the greatest tolerance. Added to their tactical sense, they have the capacity to manage others well.

The ambition of Yang Ming-earth person, when they have any, is geared to success. Success, due to social and diplomatic skills, is usually realized. But it is far from being acquired with the sacrifice that is characteristic of the Tai Yang type.

In their individual relationships they can be a great comfort to others, both a tranquilizer and entertainer, though they are not always apt at deeply penetrating the states of mind of emotive or hypersensitive persons. In their eyes such people appear to complicate their lives unnecessarily. Often their grounded, practical side earns them reproach for lack of understanding.

In love, their behavior shows no sense of drama or tragic emotion. The Yang Ming-earth is above all sensual and often remains superficial. This temperament is the least jealous and accepts for others the liberty that they afford themselves.

Because of their casual nature they are often inclined to commit errors of judgment: error in the judgment of others, whom they believe to think like they do; error in imagining, because of their enthusiasm, that events should turn in their favor. So firmly do they believe that luck is on their side that they make excessive wagers based on this belief, never realizing that they are leading themselves unconsciously to the worst possible outcomes. This impulsive behavior is also shown in their anger. It is less brutish and quick than that of Shao Yang; it is more peevish and nagging.

If there is a phlegmatic side to these individuals, all these tendencies are varied slightly, balanced by the lucidity of judgment that is typical of this character type.

Correspondence in the arts and history. Among Yang Ming-earth personalities and works, we can cite the figures of Pantagruel and Gargantua, and Sancho Pancha of Cervantes. Mister Pickwick, from Charles Dickens, is also typical, as well as Berurier from San Antonio, and Shakespeare's Falstaff. Among political figures, Nikita Khrushchev is a good example. In music, the works of Offenbach and the waltzes of Johann Strauss are typical.

Correspondence in ethnic groups and nationalities. The folklore and morals of pre-Victorian England are characteristic. The slogan of English mariners of the seventeenth century was "everything I like is illegal, immoral, or fattening."

Yang Ming-metal

General behavior. As the name indicates, the metal constitution dominates in this temperament. The physical profile is long, like a water person. The profile also resembles that of the Tai Yang, because it is naturally elegant. But the elegance of Yang Ming-metal has more of a natural than an affected air. The body and head do not appear rigid, and the movements have more natural refinement. The impression conveyed is one not of condescension but of likeable equilibrium. The great placidity is often accompanied by a penchant for pipe smoking.

The face also is long, like that of the Tai Yang. The nose is less aquiline, sometimes stronger and longer. The complexion, with age, becomes tanned like that of a sailor, the face becomes deeply wrinkled. The teeth tend to squareness. The look of the Yang Ming-metal is clear and inspires confidence. The face is impassive. Men of this type radiate a reassuring strength, like an understanding and protective father.

The Yang Ming-metal person is normally supple and agile. He or she plays sports regularly and is capable of good performance.

The constitution of this type is inclined to overheating of the yang of the large intestine and this is at the origin of vascular and infectious troubles. There are many dental caries and frequent sinusitis. The Yang Ming-metal person dreads the heat, and sometimes the cold, for the latter disturbs the intestines (colitis). However, this type of person dreads no season in particular, and prefers autumn. In food, salty tastes are preferred and milk products are greatly enjoyed.

In childhood the Yang Ming-metal person is thin, suffers from nasopharyngitis, bronchitis, and repeated rhinitis. More rarely this child is an earth child, and thus chubby, which reveals the connection between the earth and metal constitutions.

Intellectual behavior. The Yang Ming-metal person has a good memory and a good sense for exact observation. There is a preference for analysis and abstract systems like judicial law.

Psychological behavior. Yang Ming-metal persons correspond to the phlegmatic type of Berger, non-emotive and secondary. Their activities are performed with sang-froid, and it is this that makes them effective. Their work is regular and steady, without ostentation. Superficially they can appear inactive, and one is surprised to learn from their friends that these individuals "never stop."

Yang Ming-metal persons are creatures of habit; they like to order their activity as much as their conduct, and they do this with foresight and seriousness. They are individuals of principle who keep their word. They are punctual. Because of these attributes they are capable of social devotion, men and women of duty.

Of all the character types Yang Ming-metal has the most even disposition. They have a keen sense of humor, which can become capricious. The most dramatic situations are for them merely picturesque. When in conflict these individuals react with reason, setting aside subjective impressions. They analyze their problems one by one like an abstract game and methodically seek solutions.

Yang Ming-metal persons are rarely upset, and then only when an exceptional event threatens the principles on which they have built their lives. This preeminence of principles is the origin of one of their potential faults, a certain rigidity that prevents them from understanding or accepting the deviations of those who do not conform to the same principles, or those who are easily upset and are incapable of mastering their emotions.

Phlegmatic individuals have variable states of health and entrust their body to a physician as one entrusts a car to a mechanic. They are easy to care for. They only rarely feel the need to confess their inner feelings.

Correspondence in the arts and history. A Yang Ming-metal person in history would be George Washington. Notable political figures would include George Bush (with Tai Yang), Lyndon Johnson (with Shao Yang), and John Kennedy. The philosophical works of Kant, Bergson, Teilhard de Chardin, and many famous mathematicians, scientists, and doctors would also be typical. As a musical example, the works of Johann Sebastian Bach can be noted.

Correspondence in ethnic groups and nationalities. The coolness of Britannic customs, mixed with their sanguine side, characterize the Yang Ming temperament. This also explains somewhat the digestive susceptibilities of this temperament. Epidemiologic studies have shown a high frequency of ulcerative colitis among Anglo-Saxons.

The Tai Yin Temperament

Constitution. Tai Yin is the name given to the meridians of the spleen-pancreas and the lung. The Tai Yin person is of earth constitution, vulnerable in the spleen and pancreas functions, or of metal constitution, vulnerable in the functions of the lung and skin, or both at the same time.

This is an extroverted (earth) or introverted (metal) temperament. If the exclusive or dominating constitution is earth, it imprints a primary type and determines an amorphous character. Illnesses usually are digestive (pancreas) and circulatory.

In practice, there is a mix of these two character types. There is also a mix of the body types and pathologies — for example, certain obese persons who suffer from asthma, or certain thin persons who suffer from diabetes.

Tai Yin-earth

General behavior. In the Tai Yin-earth person the earth constitution dominates. The general demeanor is usually that of a large person with a squat frame, plumpness, or even obesity like that of the sanguine individual (Yang Ming-earth), its yang homologue. It is the same demeanor but with less yang. Instead of the sthenic impression of fierce energy the Tai Yin-earth person gives the impression of a rounded inertia, both in form and movement. This is the calm strength of the bull that makes haste slowly. Persons of this character are regarded as mellow, soft in their manner of speaking, acting, shaking hands, etc. Tai Yin-earth individuals can be very supple. They are not, however, athletically inclined, for they believe in exertion with the least effort.

The face is broad, round, benevolent and tranquil. It is the face of an expansive person, which corresponds with the overall morphology. The complexion is milky white or slightly pink, peach-colored. The ears or tip of the nose can be colored. The skin is soft, there is not much hair, and the face is beardless or sparsely bearded. The gaze is clear, like that of the sanguine person. The eyes are merry and light. The orbits are sometimes prominent. Together they form the stereotype of the large, absent-minded blonde with blue eyes.

115

Tai Yin-earth persons adapt to all climates, although they dread humidity or bouts of cold.

The sleep of Tai Yin-earth individuals is remarkable; they are veritable marmots. They go to sleep late, get up late, are capable of lying in bed all morning, and can take a nap under any circumstances. In a word, they like to sleep and eat.

This is the most gourmand of the temperaments. There is a preference for sweet foods, with poor regulation of the blood sugar. Sudden fatigue occurs, as well as hunger pangs several times a day, including stomach pains.

In childhood the Tai Yin-earth person is plump, delightful, of good character, easy to raise, and has a large appetite. A small speech defect can develop. Illnesses include mumps, whooping cough, enuresis, and intestinal parasites. Delayed puberty may occur, including non-descent of the testes or an absence or irregularity of periods. The Tai Yin-earth person can have a metal childhood, due to the interaction of these two temperaments, with thinness and respiratory sensitivity, nasopharyngitis, adenoids, and bronchitis.

Intellectual behavior. Tai Yin-earth individuals are endowed with an adequate memory and a faculty for drawing relationships between things. However, they do not always use this faculty in everyday life because they are absent-minded. An event, a fact, or an opportunity often escapes them.

Psychological behavior. The Tai Yin-earth type corresponds to the amorphous type of Berger: non-emotive, non-active, and primary. The Tai Yin-earth types are passive extroverts who let themselves live, and who take life on the bright side, persuaded as they are that everything will be all right. Their motto is "in life one must not worry." Extroverted, they like contact and society. They are said to have a good character because they are mild and conciliatory, never angering, and like to listen rather than speak. They do not impose their own ideas on others. One is instinctively drawn to them to speak in confidence. Their tolerance, however, is sometimes close to indifference, for their perceptions of others are received through a thick layer of non-emotivity. In terms of what concerns Tai Yin-earth persons, they are indifferent to the past, are easy-going, and harbor no malice.

116

This character type affords such individuals a certain success because they are taken as persons who have a philosophical approach to life and thus know how to live. Their absence of emotivity and partiality make others solicit them as an arbiter in conflicts of passion or merely for an opposing view. It is here that such persons like to exercise their rationalist talents, to dissect ideas and the nuances they contain, weigh the pros and cons, and finally give to the interested parties the advantages and disadvantages of each solution to try to put them right again. However, when applying this aptitude to themselves, they are sometimes unable to decide, incapable of decision, or unable to choose between two solutions that are for them often equal.

For these reasons Tai Yin-earth individuals have little ambition. Their faults include laziness and negligence. Like the fable of La Fontaine, they would rather be the cobbler than the financier. They enjoy what they have in the present. They take the time to live doing nothing, and content themselves with the strictly necessary. They tend to be neglectful, thinking they have plenty of time left, and lack punctuality because they do not know how to hurry. Faced with conflict, Tai Yin-earth persons are heavily burdened with the weight of their own inertia. They do not resist; they do not seek a solution. They wait, letting time arrange things. Like a reed, Tai Yin-earth persons bend but do not break. When the wind ceases to blow and weigh down the reed, they straighten up again and are once again lively. They have acquired an independence from authority, and feel capable of lightness and yielding in a moment to any impulses. This lightness, however, is often a part of their artistic expression, for Tai Yin-earth individuals have an aptitude for art, especially music, theater and poetry.

They have moments of enthusiasm, excessive and thoughtless, which make them obey their desires. As a consequence they are occasionally treated as children or as though they were dreamers, distracted, with their head in the clouds. In love the Tai Yin-earth person is not unconsolable, but quickly forgets one passion and seeks another, even a mediocre one.

Sometimes, however, without apparent reason, Tai Yin-earth persons have transitory periods of asthenia, are depressed, and can even become melancholic, losing their intellectual faculties and their will. At these times such persons isolate themselves and do not want to see anyone. They fall into a state of sadness and occasionally eat to compensate. But the state passes by itself, as quickly as it appeared.

They have no consistent follow-through in their resolutions. For example, they will try numerous methods to lose weight but will never follow them to the end — or simply quickly regain the lost time and pounds at the end of the dieting program.

Correspondence in the arts and history. For the Chinese, the earth is the center, the middle, the neuter. In a general way, one can cite the philosophies espousing equilibrium and the just middle as typical of Tai Yin-earth. Diogenes, Chuang Tsu, Epicurus, and Buddha are representatives. In literature La Fontaine and his fables with their numerous earth characters exhibit the Tai Yin temperament: the cobbler, Grippeminaud, the swan, etc. So too do Moliere and the characters of his dramatic works. In music, we can cite the character and music of Mozart.

Correspondence in ethnic groups and nationalities. The Asiatic folklore and temperament, mainly those of China and Cambodia, appear to be Tai Yin-earth. The word China means "land of the middle," corresponding to earth. The color of the Chinese race is yellowish, which, we may recall, is the color of the element earth. The Chinese behavior is characteristic of the Tai Yin-earth type, especially with regard to their indifference to the agitation of Westerners. Their joviality has turned the Buddha from a profound psychologist and leader of the middle path to an obese, paunchy fellow incarnating the God of goodness in an epicurean way.

Tai Yin-metal

General behavior. As its name indicates, the metal constitution dominates this temperament. The general morphology is usually long and thin. The breadth of the shoulders is narrow, the shoulders are weak, the top of the back is slightly hunched.

Tai Yin-metal individuals are asthenic in all their gestures, and in walking. Speech is slow. They have constitutional difficulties breathing, and retake their breath after long intervals via a deep respiration that is followed by a more or less noisy sigh, like that accompanying grief. (This pattern is also sometimes encountered in the Shao Yin person.)

The Tai Yin-metal person can be supple and loose or, on the contrary, markedly stiff. The temperament is sedentary, living behind closed doors and windows. In the first type the looseness of the body is that of the "rubber man," often blond and blue-eyed, with a sharp profile, milky white complexion, soft and unbearded skin. These characteristics are superimposed on the amorphous character type, with more or less apathetic traits; the nature is frivolous. The transparent quality of the expression suggests a gaze that appears to have turned to an unreal or imaginary world. Or the look may have a harsh, metallic, aspect that is disquieting to the observer.

The skin of the second type of Tai Yin-metal person, those who lack physical suppleness, is most often brownish, swarthy. The complexion is dull, the beard strong, the expression somber, the eyes chestnut-colored, the face tortuous, the nose long, the lips thin. The look seems hard and implacable, suggesting no pardon, or there are reflections of malice, calculation, hidden thought. In the latter instance the eyes give the impression that the subject suspects everyone, or present an air that inspires a lack of confidence and instinctive mistrust, or a sad and weary air.

The two morphological types usually appear in practice as mixtures of the two in various degrees. Tai Yin-metal types of persons dread above all the cold and humidity, and begin to be sick from the first signs of cold in autumn until the arrival of spring. They experience the cold in their chest and in the intestines. They often prefer to keep their head covered.

They prefer sweet tastes to salty, as well as milk products — cheese, butter, milk, yogurt. They also like piquant tastes and highly seasoned foods.

In childhood the Tai Yin-metal person is thin, pale, and fragile, and can suffer from anorexia or respiratory, cutaneous, or intestinal sensitivity. As adults these individuals may become tired easily. They feel they are chronically fatigued and complain of being unable to recuperate. They have need of frequent periods of rest, sleep, vacation. By their slowness Tai Yin-metal persons seem to economize their energy. They speak with a weak voice and do not know how to hurry. But, scrupulous and meticulous, they will, as opposed to the Tai Yin-earth type, take precautions to be punctual.

Intellectual behavior. The secondary nature of Tai Yin-metal individuals endows them with a good memory. They are capable of analyzing and drawing relations between things, and they exercise judgment with facility.

Psychological behavior. Tai Yin-metal types correspond to the apathetic type of Berger, non-emotive, non-active, and secondary. They are introverted and like to ruminate on the past. Those who tend toward the amorphous are removed from the real world and exist in an imaginary life where time is fixed. The pure apathetic type, as described by the *Nei Jing*, is closed, secretive, turned inward. Time is felt as a wearisome immobility, and is a source of anguish in their solitude.

By their slow behavior and hostility to adaptation, Tai Yin-metal persons are preservers. They do not like the unexpected and prefer to organize their lives in advance. They are sometimes slaves to their habits, ordering the smallest details of their daily lives. They are taciturn and not inclined to banal chatter. They like to establish relationships with individuals, intimate meetings with two or three people rather than large group meetings.

Prudent and cautious, Tai Yin-metal persons are economical, believing in the slogan, "a bird in the hand is worth two in the bush." By saving on a frivolous expense they experience the same satisfaction that the Jue Yin type or the diffuse, sanguine Yang Ming type would experience by indulging in a useless expense. Meticulous, they have a love of order, discipline, law. They are habitually organized, honest, rigorous. Their meticulousness encompasses their profession as well as any interest requiring precision and exactitude. Because of their innate sense of judgment, they like to exercise this ability in their profession. They cannot stop from doing so in all their relationships and on every occasion. This often leads to intolerance and slander.

It is their passion for justice and revolt against injustice that underlies their intolerance. This yearning for justice and revenge brings a tendency to begrudge. They pardon with difficulty. Their moral rigidity is expressed as implacability without appeal. There is sometimes a false appearance of conciliation, reminiscent of the slogans, "an iron hand in a velvet glove," and "the law is the law." This attitude induces the Tai Yin-metal person to go to war over imaginary enemies, like Don Quixote against windmills.

In their conflicts with others Tai Yin-metal types will react with inertia. "Their weight," says Gaston Berger, "is the staying power of their habits"(3), and it operates as much in events as in relationships.

Tai Yin-metal individuals adore reason. They cling fastidiously to details, and like to split hairs. Persuaded as they are that they have a good sense of reason, they will argue a point to the end, and seldom are they the first to be discouraged.

In love, Tai Yin-metal types are usually faithful, both in heart and mind, and are capable of devotion. Respectful of established order, they are usually observant of the legal bonds of marriage. They owe their fidelity of heart to their romantic and melancholic nature. Their tears are secret, pathetic, not ostentatious like those of the nervous Jue Yin. These latter types require consolation that the Tai Yin-metal person, sensitive and often poetic, knows how to accord as well as describe.

Faithful by reason as well as a love of the law, Tai Yin-metal individuals are opposed to transgressing bonds and prefer their world of habits and routine. This sense of fidelity, duty, and devotion is also a part of the great compassion of which the Tai Yin-metal person is capable. This feeling can give rise to a faculty of total understanding in which, paradoxically, all desire to judge their fellow creatures or to condemn disappears. Sometimes an internal struggle between this feeling of generosity without limits and the keen sensitivity to injustice makes persons of this temperament withdraw into solitude. If the sensitivity dominates the feeling of generosity, a certain misanthropy can develop, with a more marked desire for isolation. In this isolation they assemble their contradictions and abstract them to a personal philosophy. Otherwise, these contradictions can become the source of antisocial behavior where there is a desire to injure or plot. The dominating goal of Tai Yin-metal individuals, thus withdrawn into themselves and interacting only peripherally with others, resides most often, in the tranquillity that is best expressed by the proverb, "to live happily, let us live in seclusion" (3).

Tai Yin-metal types evoke the Tao of the autumn, as described in the *Nei Jing*. "The three months of autumn evoke a landing stage. One goes to bed early and gets up early. One wishes to be sedentary to palliate the rigors of autumn. One gathers in 'vital breaths' to appease the energy of autumn. One abstains from aberrant thoughts so that the energy of the lung remains pure."

When ill, Tai Yin-metal persons consult a doctor twice rather than once, follow his or her orders to the letter, and like to take medicines or potions with them wherever they go.

Correspondence in the arts and history. By morphology and image, by words, ethics, the gift of selflessness and compassion, Christ appears to be a characteristic portrait of the Tai Yin-metal personality. In the history of literature, one can cite the whole romantic period. The poetry of Verlaine is characteristic. In music, the compositions of Chopin are representative. In literature, many of the personalities in Moliere's dramas are an apathetic caricature of Tai Yin individuals. Harpagon the miser, Alceste the misanthrope, Tartuffe the deceitful, each represent diverse aspects of this type. The ideal of romanticism is found in the characters of famous stories: Cinderella, Snow White (whose complexion is evocative), Sleeping Beauty in the myth of sleep redeeming virginity and providing refuge simultaneously. The comedic team of Laurel and Hardy exemplify the thick and the thin aspects of Tai Yin.

Correspondence in ethnic groups and nationalities. The Tai Yin-metal type is typified by the Germanic people, who are characterized by moral rigidity and love of discipline. This temperament is also exemplified by the romantic spirit that is expressed by famous literary and musical talents of Germanic origin. It is tempting also to include the Scottish people in this category, a white Nordic race, large, fair-haired, with pale complexion and blue eyes.

The constitutional aspect of metal is present also in the Tai Yin temperament of the Chinese, which explains the highly developed hierarchy of traditional Chinese bureaucracy, including that found even in the organization of their ancient religious pantheon. The reputation of the Chinese temperament is as being fastidious as well as cruel and polite, but also tolerant and pacific, with a jovial spirit. These traits demonstrate the ambiguity between the amorphous aspects and the apathetic aspects of the Tai Yin. This ambiguity has produced marked fundamental oppositions and contradictions in the philosophic polarities of Chinese culture. The historic debates between the Taoists and Confucianists are another good example. These examples express the ambiguity that individuals of this temperament can feel within themselves.

General Remarks

It should again be noted that the correspondence among the temperaments and the arts, history, and ethnic groups serves only to illustrate the temperaments and the character of the persons, works, or customs that are dependent upon such temperaments. The object has not been to propose a method of identification that is only suggestive, partial, or inexact. Two persons of the same character type can be separated by an enormous gulf. It is in this difference that the personality resides, distinct from the character type.

One can easily enough determine a character type, but a real understanding of the individual personality requires the inclusion of other criteria as well. Other such criteria will be developed later in this text.

In these manipulations of symbols and analogy, one does perceive a universal language, a code that contains the truth of Chinese thought and the yin-yang doctrine. However, these thoughts and doctrines cannot be established as a science in the Cartesian sense and thereby become subject to simplistic Western reductionist methods of experimentation to verify their existence. This caution also holds true for the temperaments. We have nonetheless attempted a statistical verification, especially for the connections between disease tendency and character type, which we will refer to again in the following chapters that concern the analysis of character tests, and the use of temperaments as theoretical models for research.

Chapter 8

Relevance for the Individual

Having followed the discussion of the six temperaments in this book, the reader will have recognized the close relationship that exists between the character type and the constitution of the individual. Understanding this relationship affords one considerable knowledge about oneself, on both the physical and psychological levels.

Physical and Medical Ramifications

On the physical level, a knowledge of one's character type, hand morphology, and childhood illnesses allows you to establish a relationship with your constitutional heritage. This allows you to develop an understanding of any risks that are imposed by such an heritage. Thus, you may at times be assured that the disease or demise that claimed a parent is not a disease for which you have a constitutional predisposition. This removes an unwarranted anxiety. On the other hand, if a risk is determined, precautions can be taken.

For example, a person whose mother or father had diabetes, who was a large baby, who has remained heavy, or who has grown larger, is a person whose sanguine or amorphous character type, the Yang Ming or Tai Yin temperaments, expose them, like their parent, to diabetes. The risk will always be present in a person of such a constitution, and will be aggravated by a sedentary

125

life, overeating, and alcohol. It is reasonable for a person at risk for such a disease to take appropriate hygienic measures concerning diet and physical activity. Even here there is conflict, however, for a person of this character type is also prone to carelessness and a lack of discipline. Thus, the measures that are so clearly indicated are often difficult to follow.

The same reasoning holds for persons of constitutions that imply multiple risks, such as allergies and hay fever, arterial hypertension, heart problems, fibromas, rheumatism, or even cancer. But, rather than remaining in constant torment or in fear of being attacked by these diseases, as though stalked by an inexorable hereditary fate, you can consult a physician knowledgeable of the concepts of terrains and follow treatments for reequilibration. At least, become familiar with the early signs of the condition you fear and seek the diagnosis of a physician. Early diagnosis is almost always a benefit in determining preventive measures.

One is not bound to develop the diseases associated with a constitutional weakness. Nor will one with certainty develop phobias and other psychological conditions, or even symptoms simulating a disease. Homeopathy, herbology, plant therapy (phytotherapy), the trace elements, and acupuncture are methods, often complementary, for rectifying the existing disequilibrium.[20]

For example, bedwetting is childhood problem that is amenable to complementary therapies. Modern psychosomatic theories regard bedwetting (enuresis) as psychogenic. Western physicians will search for a renal malformation. But enuresis may be constitutional. It is a common symptom of the child of earth or metal constitution and the Tai Yin temperament. It may be discovered that one or both parents suffered from the affliction, or, if not the parents, an uncle or aunt. In any of those cases, such a discovery is an indication of the hereditary aspect of the terrains. Thus, it is more efficacious to ignore psychotherapeutic solutions and approach the syndrome by methods — such as acupuncture — that incorporate a regard for constitution.[21]

Asthma and eczema are hereditary afflictions that are also amenable to acupuncture and can be aided by a knowledge of the associated temperaments. Eczema is sometimes congenital and lasts until the age of two or three. Those afflicted with such congenital eczema should be counseled to take precautions because smallpox vaccination may be followed by the recurrence of asthma. Occasionally the parents of such a child also suffered from constitutional eczema and, following vaccination, suffered a particularly virulent attack of the disease. Such a crisis may be avoided, if the child's terrain is taken into account.

The evolution of asthma, often a hereditary disease, exemplifies the importance of terrain. It must surely be clear that the correction and reequilibration of the constitutional predisposition or terrain, which can bring about a significant amelioration or even a cure for this condition, is preferable to the symptomatic relief provided by the medications prescribed for shortness of breath. It is also preferable to the desensitization to the substances that produce the allergy.

Other aspects of a knowledge of the temperaments require only personal observation and reflection. For example, certain enthusiastic Shao Yang or nervous Jue Yin persons, who are predisposed to viral hepatitis, display not only the chronic fatigue that is associated with these infections, but also an aggravation of certain eye problems, like myopia or chronic conjunctivitis. (In classical medicine, however, this relationship between the eye and liver is unrecognized, so much so that the physician generally does not lend an attentive ear to the complaints of these patients.) Also following hepatitis the menstrual periods may be more painful and migraine attacks more frequent. As we have seen in studying the wood constitution, the liver is linked to the ovary and to cephalic regions through the course of its meridian.

It is also possible that this characteristic fatigue may be accompanied by renewed nervousness, instability, hypersensitivity to the smallest noise, and muscular spasms. The slightly nervous woman may become extremely upset during repeated periods of stress corresponding with having taken the contraceptive pill for several months. She may also suffer from bouts of muscular spasms or tetany. The relationships of stress, liver, spasms, and the contraceptive pill are readily recognized by the acupuncturist. The origin of the disequilibrium is more understandable, the natural weaknesses associated with this terrain are recalled. In this case it is the hepatic terrain that is indicated, and there are appropriate measures that may be instituted. For example, the contraceptive pill would be stopped, several weeks of rest recommended, and an anti-stress regimen developed.

If an individual is not made aware of the underlying relationships that exist between the afflictions that may follow a bout of hepatitis, or the contraceptive pill, and the risk of spasms, aggravated myopia, or even an obstinate acne, it is unlikely that he or she will be disposed to make even the most basic changes of habit. For example, simple changes in dietary regimen might be ignored or put off. It is astounding the number of people affected by this condition, who persist in drinking coffee, or consuming chocolate bars every day or several times a week. Neither the best physician in the world nor the most brilliant diagnosis can be of any help, if the person continues consuming such veritable poisons of the liver.

What is crucial for the individual to recognize is that there is a predisposition to illness that can be understood in the context of the terrain and the temperament. Using this association, a variety of illnesses can be seen to result from a common stimulus. One person who drinks alcohol to excess will develop cirrhosis of the liver, another delirium tremens, another chronic pancreatitis, stomach ulcer, or multiple neuritis of the arms and legs. One person who smokes excessively may develop an infarction or arteritis, while another may develop emphysema or lung cancer.

Psychological Ramifications

The advantage of understanding one's character and psychology is appreciated by all. Every civilization has emphasized the Socratic directive: Know thyself. To know your character is to know your strengths as well as weaknesses. Most individuals understand only the dominant elements of their character, and are aware of contradictions they cannot explain. This is even more true in our perception of others. All too often, the image we have of the friends and individuals around us is one that is short-sighted and rudimentary. We judge by appearance and, more exactly, by only the most obvious appearance.

Each individual is affected by a dominant type that acts more or less despotically on the personality. There are as well various tendencies of the character that are contradictory. It is therefore useful to know both the dominant and secondary character types to understand the melange of coherencies and incoherencies, potentials and inhibitions.

In more than 60% of cases, character types are composed of complexes such as passionate and amorphous, apathetic and nervous, nervous and sentimental, enthusiastic and phlegmatic, sanguine and sentimental, etc. In the complexes the tendencies oppose each other to better create the nuances and richness of character. It is this richness that creates the range of adaptations to diverse situations and relationships.

To know oneself in the context of these nuances permits an understanding of oneself, even one's contradictions, and explains why at certain times an individual may be affected by depression without apparent reason, or contrarily by excessive enthusiasm, or, even by indifference to everything. Such mood fluctuations become clear when considered in the light of the temperaments. Understanding is gained without the necessity of recourse to psychoanalysis (although this does not deny the validity of psychoanalytic interpretations, as we shall see later on.)

It is interesting to establish a distinction between the character and the personality. As traditionally defined, the character is a set of habitual patterns of behavior and modes of reaction distinguishing one individual from another. To know these sets of behaviors it is necessary to know the tendencies of each character type. The personality, however, is that aspect of a person that expresses individuality. In psychology, personality is regarded as that function by which a conscious individual perceives him- or herself as an "I," a uniquely existing individual.

Many people confuse their character with their personality. For example, a person may be proud of his or her tendency to react quickly, to resolve challenges even at the price of fighting. This person may be content to have an aggressive and strong personality. This assumed "personality" is, in terms of acupuncture, a character type, and, specifically, the enthusiastic character type of the Shao Yang temperament. On the physiological level, this temperament is subtended by a tonic activity of the hepatobiliary function in conjunction with the thyroid gland.

Another person may see him- or herself as having a strong personality because of his or her desire to dominate, to expend industriously the time requisite for the completion of tasks, and in controlling him- or herself in the most vigorous fashion. This is a description of a passionate character type of the Tai Yang temperament that, physiologically, is subtended by a tonic activity of the bladder and gonad function, and is related to the sexual organs and the adrenal glands.

A third person may say he or she has a strong personality because he or she does not take sides and does not engage in useless discussion. This person is wary of the ambitions that drive men to their ruin; he or she adopts a formula for living in the present, from day to day. This is the amorphous character of the Tai Yin-earth temperament. Physiologically it is subtended by the hypotonic endocrine and hypertonic exocrine (digestive) functions of the pancreas.

This confusion of personality and character is the source of many ills, the principal one undoubtedly being the opposition that pervades so much of human interaction. If the personality is the function by which the individual conceives the "I," this does not necessarily imply that one must identify oneself with the tendencies of comportment that constitute this "I."

The definition of a strong personality as put forth by Lalande is perhaps more appropriate. He defines such a person as "one realizing more or less the superior qualities by which that person distinguishes him- or herself from a simple biological individual." By this definition one may see that the personality is perceived in relation to the character type.

The study of character types and temperaments provides some easily comprehensible and immediate advantages. Firstly, we can gain a certain humility, realizing that our most distinctive, individual behaviors are often in direct rapport with our biological activities, and that these patterns are shared with persons of like constitution. Secondly, we can realize that certain of our mental disequilibria, especially those in times of crisis, depend on biologic variations that have determinable or patternable causes. Such causes can be stress, dietary errors, excessively sedentary behavior, abuse of stimulants; or causes independent of our intentions, like climatic variations or diverse cosmic influences; or, more basically, our cultural surroundings, our social and work milieu, etc. This knowledge can provide opportunities for self-directed correction of longstanding physical and psychological problems. A third advantage is the encouragement of self-confidence. To know oneself better permits one to be more responsible for self and others, as well as to recognize essential differences between oneself and others. Ordinarily, depending on character, differences from others may be felt painfully, incomprehensibly, or even indifferently. The incompatibilities that exist between character types and temperaments are at the origin of conflicts among people, whether in their emotional or professional lives.

The ideas expressed by ancient Chinese psychology even extend into the domain of marriage, giving guidelines for the choice of a spouse. The method is still utilized today in the Orient. The man is yang, the woman yin. Each may be classified according to five types based on the five elements, and each corresponds to a specific mix of the five constitutions and hand morphologies. Normally, the yang man should dominate the yin woman. It should be understood that this is not a mere phallocratic chauvinism, but the result of the observation of complementarity between masculinity, which in its normal state is manifested as a natural virility, and femininity, which in its natural state is manifest by receptivity. The implication involves cosmic order rather than simple social control and is finely expressed by the creative - receptive duality discussed in the *I Ching*.

In practice, the two laws of the five elements are used for calculation of the appropriate combination. Whatever element the man may be, compatibility with a woman will be based on the element that his corresponding element engenders or dominates. For example, if a man is wood, the ideal companion for him is considered to be a woman of fire or earth constitution, or of the same element as he, wood. Inversely, for a woman, the ideal companion is a man corresponding to the element that precedes her constitutional association in the five element system. For a woman of wood, a man of water constitution, or one who dominates her, a man of metal constitution, or a man of the same element, would be considered well chosen.

The five elements in their opposition to one another also correspond to opposed behaviors. For example, the first four constitutions or temperaments in the following table are emotive types; the last four are non-emotive types. In terms of the harmony of couples, there is a frequent association between an emotive female and a non-emotive male. Conversely a non-emotive female is frequently associated with an emotive male. The same complementarities exist for activity and resonance. However, if the opposition is too great, the character types can clash. If the similarity is too great, the character types can be too inhibitory.

Character Type	Temperament	Element & Organ			
Passionate	Tai Yang	Fire	SI	Water	BL
Enthusiastic	Shao Yang	Wood	GB	Fire	TB
Sentimental	Shao Yin	Water	KI	Fire	HT
Nervous	Jue Yin	Wood	LV	Fire	PC
Sanguine	Yang Ming	Earth	ST		
Phlegmatic	Yang Ming	Metal	LI		
Amorphous	Tai Yin	Earth	SP		
Apathetic	Tai Yin	Metal	LU		

Happily, nature is usually more complex. As we have seen, individuals consist of one dominating constitution, one dominating temperament, and secondary constitutions and temperaments. An understanding of the makeup of individuals thus allows us to understand the bases for compatibilities as well as incompatibilities.

When certain incompatibilities are too great and the character type of one is bullied by that of the other, the physiologic disorders that may result are best understood by reference to the psychosomatic laws of acupuncture. It is even possible to suggest that an individual composed of two equal constitutional types will develop pathological consequences in one or the other constitutional type according to their conjugal incompatibilities. Such consequences will be manifest if the conflict is great and finally dominates the harmony.

The same consequences can occur in professional life where there are hierarchical relationships. The superior who is an unreasonable character and abuses his or her authority can create physiological disorders in the workers with whom the superior has failed to associate harmoniously. For example, a passionate Tai Yang person of water constitution, a stubborn, authoritarian character, will be more easily guided and commanded by a phlegmatic Yang Ming person: metal engenders water. The phlegmatic person will make his or her remarks and directives with more humor than uproar, and will not convey an impression of stern authority.

But water engenders wood, and the Tai Yang person will not like the authority of the enthusiastic Shao Yang wood constitution because water has authority over wood. Inversely, some individuals need to be prodded. The amorphous Tai Yin of earth constitution will like the enthusiastic authority of the Shao Yang (wood dominates earth). Such authority will take the amorphous person out of his or her torpor and induce a desire to accomplish missions for which he or she ordinarily would not have ambition.

On the other hand, there can arise certain somatic problems as a result of the conflict in compatibilities, such as the classic ulcer formation in a stubborn subordinate placed under the excessive authority of a boss. Uneasiness, in a hierarchical superior, can also be the result of finding in a subordinate a capacity for initiative that is equal to that of the superior. The same sense of discomfort can arise in couples where the man feels an unfulfilled virility because of his domination by a woman, or in which the woman feels unfulfilled in her femininity because of the insufficiency of her partner.

Counsels for Your Constitutional Type

Shao Yang — Enthusiastic

Wood and Fire (Gallbladder and Triple Burner)

Physical: Sports are, for you, an excellent way to maintain your balance of health. They provide the necessary exercise that is important to your muscles. Competitive sports are perhaps ideal, as you have a love of competition. If you take up a sport after a long period of idleness or disuse, don't be too impulsive; make regular, steady progress.

Alimentary: Eat fewer acidic or spicy foods, consume less stimulants such as coffee or cigarettes; drink less alcohol. Your habit is to function with the help of stimulants, consuming additional quantities whenever you experience an energy slump. You should try to find a way to regularize your energy without recourse to the trepidations of drug stimulants.

Psychological: If you are of a wood constitution, you must work at controlling your impulsiveness, your impatience, and your anger. Your challenge: though tolerant and understanding, your nervous system doesn't help you. You end up being impatient with the slowness of others or upset with them. You must learn to outmaneuver your nervous system, learning to see the anger or impatience before it takes control of you.

If you are of a fire constitution, learn to control your enthusiasm. You are carried away by ideas, objects, individuals. Say to yourself, "I will not make instantaneous decisions, I will let some time pass while the air settles."

Jue Yin — Nervous
Wood and Fire (Liver and Pericardium)

Physical: Whether you like or dislike physical activity, you need it. If you enjoy sports, take the time to do them, for as soon as you are outside, you will feel better. Don't stay by yourself in a closed room smoking or daydreaming! If you don't care so much for sports, find an activity such as dance, exercise, or martial arts (tai chi, qi gong, kung fu, karate, etc.).

Alimentary: Because chocolate can easily perturb your body and your nerves, it would be a good idea to limit how much of it you consume.

Psychological: You love to dream, to fantasize. You enjoy theaters, lectures, movies. Give yourself the time and the right to be original, sensitive, creative; for that is your deepest nature, vibrant and feeling. Keep on your good side, don't heap blame on yourself. Don't let your emotional excesses, your eccentricities, control you. Cultivate self-control and play with viewing the turmoil of emotions inside of you as if you were an actor in a theater. The actor is not his part: he plays.

Don't succumb to distress and lack of self-confidence. As you naturally recover your contact with your self, with the sensations of the moment, if you work on developing your awareness of the boundaries of your physical self, and speculate on the how and the why of your problems, you will be able to more quickly control these feelings of anguish or lack of confidence.

Tai Yang — Passionate

Fire and Water (Small Intestine and Bladder)

Physical: You must make your spinal column more supple and take care of it to avoid lumbar blockages, sciatica, or torticollis (wry neck).

Alimentary: Don't abuse alcohol or intake of salty foods. You can at times be temperate and abstemious and at times totally profligate; learn to control these impulses.

Psychological: Endowed with great intellectual capabilities and a good memory, you are very stubborn and self-willed. Your motto is, "What I want to do, I will do." Understand that this is possible for you because this is your nature. But be tolerant with regard to others less willful or less ambitious than you.

Your challenge: You would do well to learn from others some modesty, humility, patience. Try to accept the criticisms of others and learn to thank them for helping you to see your mistakes and failures.

Shao Yin — Sentimental

Water and Fire (Kidney and Heart)

Physical: You are easily sensitive to cold and don't care much for sports. Like the Jue Yin, look for an activity that will get your energy moving, for example dance, exercise, or martial arts. You don't need to start boxing or weight-lifting, or any competitive sport, just get moving.

Your body is instinctively fearful. You can gradually overcome this by involving yourself in sports or physical activities where audacity is necessary. Simply undertake walking at a rapid pace, winter and summer alike, wearing minimal clothing. Gradually acclimate yourself to a less fearful relationship with nature, and a more robust attitude.

Alimentary: Decrease your salt intake. Keep an eye on your taste for pork — ham, bacon, sausage, etc. If you are a Shao Yin who overindulges in sweets and pastries, it's a good idea to cut back your consumption of these treats.

Psychological: Other persons have a sensitivity less developed than yours; they cannot understand you and are not the way you wish them to be. Don't turn in on yourself and think yourself to be as misunderstood as a martyr. Fear makes you see danger and defeat where they are not. Venture cautiously at first, but be a little braver each time. You will see that success arrives and "luck" will turn in your favor.

Your challenge: dare to live. If you are afraid of life or sometimes loose the taste and the sense of life, then everything will seem absurd. This is a perception that goes on within you; it is not existence itself that lacks interest. Look around you, look to nature. The animals don't ask themselves these questions. They live. They follow their fundamental momentum. Rediscover your fundamental momentum, your vital force. If you are astray in the dark, at the edge of a precipice, then turn towards nature, towards the living things in nature, and you will find the contact that you have only momentarily lost.

Yang Ming-Earth — Sanguine

Earth (Stomach)

Physical: You are endowed with a good constitution, but you are not invulnerable. Take up a sport or an energetic activity. It is the best way for you to avoid or diminish your tendency to arterial hypertension and arteriosclerosis.

Alimentary: Moderation is difficult for you. With great ease you can consume too much food, too many sauces, too much salt, alcohol, coffee, sugar, milk, beer. Try to leave the table while still a little hungry. Your weight will lessen, your body will become lighter, you will feel better.

Psychological: Don't always take everything as such a lark, be serious from time to time. Respect sensitive individuals who don't have your sturdy exterior. Your challenge: to help others to communicate and to be at peace.

Tai Yin-Earth — Amorphous
Earth (Spleen)

Physical: Bestir yourself a bit more. Train yourself to sleep less, and give yourself a routine with at least a minimal physical activity: walking at a brisk pace is enough, if no other activity interests you.

Alimentary: If you have realized that your favorite foods are sugar, milk, and dairy products such as cheese, learn also to realize that you would help your health by limiting your intake of these foods.

Psychological: Try to not think too much or to deliberate too long before acting - or instead of acting.

Your challenge: make decisions and to follow them through. You are well suited to understand others and to give them advice. Follow some of your own advice!

Yang Ming-Metal — Phlegmatic
Metal (Large Intestine)

Physical: Of robust constitution, you could be lithe and lissom if you wished. You must learn to respect your body's deeply felt need for regular activity.

Alimentary: The foods most damaging to you are milk, spicy foods, alcohol. It is a good idea for you to enjoy more raw fruits and vegetables.

Psychological: Full of humor and straight-faced gags, you can at times appear cold and overly rational. Make an effort to go and meet hypersensitive persons and help them to live their emotions.

Your challenge: Share in the feelings of others rather than requiring them to always control their emotions.

Tai Yin-Metal — Apathetic
Metal (Lung)

Physical: You must make an effort to get out of the house, for you enjoy being indoors. Your body has need of activity; take up walking, skiing, mountain climbing, or jogging.

Alimentary: Try to eat less yogurt, milk, and cheese. Consumption of fruit, legumes, and raw vegetables ought also to be limited. If you feel the cold easily, try eating a little more meat, fish, or eggs.

Psychological: You are meticulous and precise in your analysis, but you judge too quickly.

Your challenge: if you can accept the idea that others are different from you and react differently to situations, if you can also accept that good and bad have the same right to exist, just as day and night, and that it follows a universal law just as the yin-yang of the Taoists, then you will be less bitter and solitary, and more open and happy — all the more so because you are greatly capable of devotion and self-sacrifice.

Evaluating the Results of the Tests

Having determined your primary and secondary constitutions, and your dominant and secondary character, you may have found, as is most often the case, that your character corresponds to your constitution. If your constitution is wood, your character is enthusiastic, Shao Yang, or nervous, Jue Yin. If your constitution is water, your dominant character is sentimental, Shao Yin, or passionate, Tai Yang. There are, however, classic exceptions: the earth constitution is sometimes linked to the passionate character, as was the probably case with Orson Welles.

There are other cases where the primary constitutions do not match the dominant character, but match the traits of the second or third most dominant character. There are even cases where the dominant character corresponds to the secondary constitution. This situation is normal and is how one distinguishes the constitution from the temperaments. The constitutions are invariable. Like a physical endowment the changes of age and circumstance have their slow, but consistent effects. The temperaments are variable but within the "possibilities" of the constitution.

Suppose an individual's constitution is wood, water, and metal, and the temperament is found to be mixed Shao Yin (sentimental), Shao Yang (enthusiastic), and Yang Ming-metal (phlegmatic). The order of temperament is different than the order of constitution. It depends on many variables: location, climate, profession, age, maturity, eating habits, activities, personality of the partner, past illnesses or operations — in short, the circumstances of life.

In our example, this enthusiastic, sentimental individual may have just experienced a great sorrow and the strength of his or her sentimental temperament may have overtaken the enthusiastic character. We must not therefore assume that the temperaments are invariable, but follow them with interest, regarding the vagaries of comportment as a function of life. By contrast, if a person with an earth constitution in last place also has a Tai Yin temperament in last place, we cannot suppose for an instant that this individual will some day exhibit this amorphous character as the dominant trait. This variable of comportment is possible, but within definite limits, not likely.

To have an idea of your behavioral tendencies, you should align two, or even three main character types, and assume occasional rearrangements of their order. If you are most interested in determining your constitutional type, you can reliably accept, in a direct fashion, the scores from the Hand Analysis and Childhood Symptoms. This is expressed as the cumulative results documented on Table 4 (page 74). On the other hand, the analysis of temperament from Table 5 (page 76), represents a range of probabilities that will vary with the conditions of your life.

A Sample Case History

The following actual case example is one of the cases studied while testing the information and procedures in chapter 5. While there are many case histories in the files of practitioners who use the systems presented in this book, you are probably seeking personal and preventive counsel, rather than a treatment for a specific illness. This sample involves a fairly complex set of test scores and allows you to follow their refinement. Thus, this case provides you with an example of how even complex character analysis can be accomplished with some time and study.

The subject is a 25-year old female, in good health, with several general health concerns and personal conflicts, yet no manifest illness. As in most cases, the symptoms and complaints are not particularly specific and could have many possible causes. Her lifestyle includes a wholistic approach to health and some self-development practices, but no extreme, long-established practices.

Results of the Sample Hand Analysis Tests

The answers to the first test reveal a predominance of yang:

Is Your Hand Yin or Yang?			
Question	Yin/Yang	Score	
		Yin	Yang
Is your handshake soft and wavering?	Yes = Yin		1
Is your handshake firm and vigorous?	Yes = Yang		1
Are your hands cold?	Yes = Yin	.5	.5
Are your hands warm?	Yes = Yang	.5	.5
Are your hands pale, yellowish or blue?	Yes = Yin	1	
Are your hands red or well colored?	Yes = Yang		1
Totals		1	5

From this we can expect that the overall comportment will relate to the yang temperaments — Tai Yang, Shao Yang, or Yang Ming.

The results of the hand structure analysis fill in more details:

Table One: Hand Analysis Results						
Total Points	Characteristics	Elements				
		Wood	Fire	Earth	Metal	Water
5	1. Overall shape				5	
3	2. Shape of nail				1	
1	3. Finger characteristics	1.5	1.5			
1	4. Specific characteristics	1			1	
10	Totals	2.5	1.5		7	

The wood and fire scores suggest Shao Yang or Jue Yin as likely temperaments, with the predominance of yang in the preceding test making Shao Yang more likely. Metal constitutions are often related to Yang Ming or Tai Yin temperaments, but the yang tendency suggests Yang Ming.

Results of the Sample Childhood Symptoms Test

The results of the childhood symptoms test are inconclusive. The low metal score is contrary to the metal scores the subject gave herself in the hand test. The majority of the responses are in the wood category, followed by fire. Thus, we see the wood constitution again, and can think of temperaments including the wood element. These were evidenced by the hand morphology, but to a lesser extent than metal. So far, the indication is for a mixed temperament, with yang predominant, and a mixed constitution with wood, fire, and metal elements.

Table Two: Evaluation of Childhood Symptoms		
Element	*Affliction*	*Points*
Wood	Digestive intolerances or allergies (eggs, chocolate)	✔1
	Abnormal acetone levels in blood	1
	Nearsightedness	✔2
	Nail-biting	1
	Hives or seasonal asthma	✔1
	Viral hepatitis, neonatal jaundice, or fetal suffering	1
	Total Points	4
Metal	Inflammation of the nose and throat, larynx, or trachea	✔1
	Severe ear inflammation without pus	1
	Bronchitis	1
	Winter asthma	2
	Bedwetting	1
	Lateral curvature of the spine (scoliosis)	1
	Total Points	1
Fire	Bouts of uncontrollable sobbing	1
	Fever to 104 °F	✔2
	Convulsions	1
	Epilepsy	1
	Thoracic pain (angina) - esp. in summer	2
	Total Points	2
Water	Orthostatic albuminuria	1
	Repeated anginas	2
	Suppurating earaches or mastoiditis	1
	Impetigo or boils	1
	Viral or bacterial infections	✔1
	Bedwetting	1
	Total Points	1
Earth	Intestinal parasites	1
	Fungal infections	1
	Frequent hiccups or stomach complaints	✔2
	Dislocation of the testicle	1
	Late puberty	1
	Bedwetting	1
	Total Points	2

The results of the CE-40 confirm the mixed temperament picture given by the preceding tests:

141

Table Three: CE-40 Test Scores			
Character	Score	Character	Score
1. Shao Yang	45	4. Jue Yin	34
2. Tai Yang	40	5. Tai Yin Metal	30
3. Yang Ming Earth	37	6. Yang Ming Metal	17

This shows that the character will not be among the nearly fifty percent of tests that evidence a pure character type; in fact, it is among the more complex possibilities with the first three scores all relatively close to each other. The fire and wood scores from the hand and childhood symptoms tests relate to the Shao Yang temperament, and the fire constitution is shared by the first two and most important temperaments. The high metal scores on the hand tests don't appear except in the lowest two temperaments. Thus, the metal component of the constitution looks less important, but this may reflect only the current circumstances.

This mixed type of character is among the more complex possible. Here we can expect that the Shao Yang temperament overshadows Tai Yang and Yang Ming, or that the dominant temperament is colored by one or both of these secondary temperaments. However, we should expect that the range of possibilities includes aspects of the first four temperaments. All three of the yang temperaments indicate activity; Tai Yang and Shao Yang are both emotive types, only Yang Ming is non-emotive. So, an active and emotive tendency should be strong.

The compiled scores, which refine all the scores by taking account of relative importance, make the wood-fire constitutional tendency more obvious:

Table Four: Compilation of Test Results						
Your constitutional classification						
Table	Final Score	Wood	Fire	Earth	Metal	Water
1	from your Hand Analysis	4	3		7	
2	from Childhood Symptoms	7	4	3	2	2
3	from your CE-40 Test	7	3+4			3
3	CE-40 Test (1st or 2nd place tied)					
	TOTAL	15	14	3	9	5

This can be displayed graphically as follows:

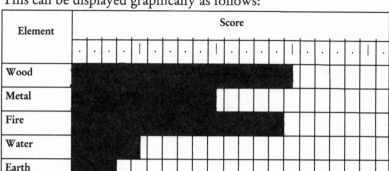

Note: each dot equals 1 point, the bars 5 points; if any score is over 25 points, divide all scores by two before plotting.

The temperaments are charted with the following results:

Table Five — Temperament Summary					
Rank	Temperament	CE-40 Score	Yin-Yang	Element	Total
1	Shao Yang	45	2	1	48
2	Tai Yang	40	2	1	43
3	Yang Ming-Earth	37	2	0	39

This can be plotted as follows, after dividing by two to fit the space available:

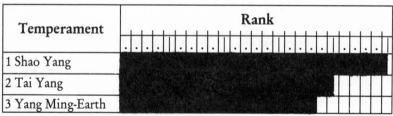

Note: each dot equals 1 point, the bars 5 points; if any score is over 25 points, divide all scores by two before plotting.

While the character is still complex, the emphasis is clearly yang, active, emotive. The gallbladder, heart, small intestine (wood, fire, Shao Yang, Tai Yang), and the stomach (Yang Ming-earth) organs are most indicated. The axis of the constitution is wood—fire, with a strong metal undercurrent that may color the expression of a trait, or appear as a metal vulnerability. We can expect a Shao Yang temperament more or less modified by Tai Yang and Yang Ming qualities.

The lack of a metal element in any of the three temperaments and the lack of an earth element in the hand analysis would be sufficient reason to go back and examine the results of the hand morphology test, or reevaluate the responses to the CE-40 questionnaire. There may have been a misjudgement between metal and earth. However, this may also point toward a familial metal tendency that is constitutional, but dominated by the current temperaments which are more subject to the changes of life.

It is important to remember that the studies on which the CE-40 is based (see chapter 10), show that single character determinations are very accurate, but with multiple character scores, such as this example, it is reasonable to question whether the self-analysis was too subjective. In other words, the answers to the questions may have been more what the subject believed, or wanted to think, and less what a more objective observer might have discovered. Regardless of the degree of difficulty in determining multiple temperament with great accuracy, a final assessment from a comparison of symptoms, likes, and dislikes can be very useful.

The subject's list of self-recognized aspects includes these:

Main Physical Complaints

Poor digestion (gas, constipation, diarrhea)
Skin conditions (acne, hives, boils)

Main Psychological/Intellectual Concerns

Worry, related to loneliness, but not completely so
Difficulty learning, needs to learn by doing
Difficulty concentrating
Difficulty committing to something
No clear preference for life work
Feels capable of anything, but has trouble deciding what to do
Desires confirmation from others "that I'm good at it"

Physical Habits

Sleeps well and a lot (8-9 hours)
Goes to be early, gets up early
"Snacks a lot"
Needs breakfast

Likes

Sweets
Coffee (leading to digestive and complexion problems)
Autonomy
Sensuality
Movies
Reading
Lovemaking
Eating
Art
Music

Dislikes

Rules
Conventionality ("normal" society)
Banks and bureaucracies
Poor quality
Stupid people
Heat
Humidity
Spicy foods

From chapter 6, we can see that the wood constitution is subject to liver and gallbladder troubles. The digestive problems reported are often linked to these organs and may also be linked to skin irritations. These are consistent with wood and fire. There is an indication of allergic reactions, which can also lead to skin conditions, and is seen in the childhood history. The gallbladder sensitivity of the wood constitution is a very probable source of these problems.

The "early to bed and early to rise" habit is not linked to wood, and is one of the shadings provided by the earth and metal elements behind the fire and wood. The impatience, wavering concentration, difficulty in chosing and keeping with one's choices are all strongly related to both wood and fire, Shao Yang.

In short, the wood–fire axis, the organs it indicates, and the compiled test scores all point to a wood–fire constitutional predominance. This is further confirmed by reading chapter 7.

The strong active, emotive components of the two primary temperaments, Shao Yang and Tai Yang, are clearly evidenced. The dislike of heat, rather than fear of cold, the overabundance of ideas, disorderly concentration, and impatience of the Shao Yang are clear. (This was clear on the tests themselves, where the handwritten grids and tables had many "cross-outs," math errors, etc. — all signs of too quick a response, and impatient reactions.) The sensual, artistic, and social characteristics the subject reported are also typical of a Shao Yang.

The secondary Tai Yang temperament, a fire and water constitution, supports the active and emotive aspects of the primary Shao Yang temperament. This suggests that some of the subject's traits are hyperexcitability, and an overemphasis on intellectual movement instead of more productive concentration. The difficulty choosing lifework, etc., may be smoothed-over by the Tai Yang concentration on a significant goal, or conversely hindered by that temperament's tendency to "look down" on others. This too may contribute to a feeling of loneliness, despite the strong Shao Yang sociability. Rebellious, stubborn, and self-willed, the subject's dislike for "stupidity" may also contribute to a feeling of loneliness. Shao Yang subjects frequently express distaste for contrary authority (banks, bureaucracies), and limits (desire for autonomy).

The Shao Yang sensuality is supported by the robust appetite of Yang Ming-earth. Both enjoy excitement and the "the good life." This combination may not be all that constructive for a gallbladder-sensitive constitution. This is particularly true because we have seen in this chapter that stimulants — coffee, sweets, alcohol — are in particular need of moderation for all three of the subject's temperaments, and both predominant constitutions.

An obvious need, particularly with such an active subject, is to repair the lack of sport and exercise — there are no active aspects in the list of the subject's favorite activities. Tai chi, or swimming, an activity to work on the lateral rigidity to which Shao Yang are predisposed, and the spinal stiffness contributed by the Tai Yang component, would be excellent choices for this subject. These activities will also improve the hypertension and arteriosclerotic problems that come from Yang Ming-earth.

Also, dietary temperance is a clear need that will improve the subject's long term health. While young now, the disposition toward digestive problems can only increase with age and lead to more serious illnesses. The reactions now expressed superficially, may later turn to internal, and more dangerous problems. However, the lack of discipline, and the excitement of the moment, to which the Shao Yang and Yang Ming-earth temperaments dispose, suggest that extreme disciplines should be avoided — both to modify the extremism of these temperaments and to recognize their difficulty in staying with a regimen. Perhaps the stubbornness of the Tai Yang character can be called on for help.

There is also a strong artistic and expressive component in the Shao Yang temperament. Here too are possibilities for productive use of an active sensuality and sensitive emotions. The bellicose nature could be moderated with social leadership roles, putting the aggressivity and exaggerated sense of self-importance to good work. This would make good use of the Tai Yang authoritativeness, and the Yang Ming-earth sociability. Periods of rest and relaxation, quiet meditation, or dedication to an intellectual pursuit of some difficulty (along with exercise and a more moderate diet) could be of great benefit.

Here, clearly, the discipline, attachment to goals, and will power of the secondary Tai Yang temperament need to be turned from their expression as resistance to the direction or discipline of others, and toward self-direction and discipline. Intellectually, and psychologically, a large, difficult, and self-chosen goal (and the intellectual and dietary discipline it would bring) — drawn from the Tai Yang — to support the primary enthusiasm of the Shao Yang, would be an excellent, positive, and helpful adaptation well within the tendencies of the subject's character.

So we see that even with a complex, three-tiered set of temperaments, it is possible to find ways to practically and effectively ameliorate your deficits and predispositions with the constructive tendencies indicated by your constitution and temperament.

Chapter 9

Relevance for the Acupuncturist

A more complete discussion of the relevance of temperament to acupuncture has been developed my work, *Terrains and Pathology in Acupuncture.* In brief, two principal points can be noted. First, the idea of temperament, as put forth by acupuncture, in combination with the characterology of Berger, provides the acupuncturist with a more accurate patient psychological profile than those obtained from current acupuncture texts.

The second is that the numerous symptoms and diseases that are associated with a constitution and its respective element are usually studied separately, somewhat like disease in Western medicine. Separation of symptoms and diseases is based on the energetic aspects of physiology: there is an excess or emptiness of energy, an excess of yang or yin, a vacancy of one or the other. There is also blood in relation to energy, disequilibrium in the circulation of the meridians related to the corresponding functions, with an excess of energy in the top or lower part of the body, on one side or the other, or on the interior to the detriment of the exterior, etc. Intermixed with the physiological symptoms are psychological and physical symptoms, problems of one or another organ caused by heat or cold, or a particular mood.

The advantage of analyzing symptoms through constitutions and temperaments is that it prioritizes these different troubles, and allows the acupuncturist to group all the symptoms according to respective functions on the one hand, and to understand the exceptional coherency that exists in the circulation of the meridians, on the other.

Thus we find that vertigo, anger, hypertension, migraines, emotional tachycardia, anxiety, and spasms are examples of problems of the liver and gallbladder meridians, of the wood constitution. Because the Shao Yang and Jue Yin meridians are coupled like the inside and outside of a garment, one can take the diagnosis further and declare that the origin of all these problems is a single disorder: a repletion of yang in one meridian, with energy directed toward the top of the body, from which come cephalic symptoms. There is a complimentary depletion of yin in the other meridian, as well as an emptiness of blood, which explains the association of these problems with venous circulation troubles in the lower legs, hemorrhoids, and congestion in the uterus leading to painful periods.

On the therapeutic level, the measures the acupuncturist must take are obvious: reequilibration of the meridians by the insertion of needles into the appropriate acupuncture points, and, possibly, prescription of the corresponding trace element. By these interventions it is not only a symptom that the acupuncturist dispels, but a whole group of related problems. On the surface the maneuvers are therapeutic, but in reality such maneuvers have preventive consequences, since they become corrections of the entire terrain. The concept of terrain is thus at the core of the method the acupuncturist must use to understand and care for a patient.

Since its inception acupuncture has enjoyed a reputation for being a preventive medicine. One ancient anecdote relates that certain Chinese social classes consulted their physician regularly, and paid their services so long as the family members were in good health. But, the family ceased paying the physician when they became ill. Unfortunately, the general aim of medicine today is to repair the body after illness, rather than to prevent the occurrence of illness. Yet the concept of the temperaments, if applied appropriately, is efficacious not only for prevention but also for repair. An understanding of the patient, which includes an understanding of the temperament, character type, and constitution, permits a greater understanding of the nature of the illness, and the therapeutic approaches most likely to succeed.

Two examples of disease processes illustrate this point: colitis and hypertension. When a patient consults a physician about colitis, there are varieties of colitis identified in Chinese medicine, just as there are variable types in Western medicine, that must be differentiated. They are classed by the time of onset, the nature of the symptoms, and the nature of the aggravating conditions.

A single origin, however, does not result in random variety. The colitis of the Shao Yang enthusiastic type occurs more frequently in the right colon and is associated with sharp pain, alternating constipation and diarrhea, and, frequently, hemorrhoids. The origin according to acupuncture is an excess of the gallbladder meridian, with sporadic biliary flushing provoking attacks of diarrhea. The condition is aggravated by rich foods cooked in fat, a favorite of the Shao Yang individual. The colitis of the Tai Yin amorphous type, however, while also on the right side, is associated with abdominal bloating and chronic rather than sporadic constipation. The condition is aggravated by raw fruits and vegetables, which the person is inclined to consume to excess. The colitis of the Tai Yin apathetic or of the Yang Ming phlegmatic is predominantly on the left side, the constipation is obstinate, and the symptoms tend to be permanent. The condition is aggravated by excessive consumption of milk products and yogurt. (This can also be true for the Tai Yin amorphous person.)

A knowledge of temperament can often lead to a diagnosis of the particular form of a disease. The treatment proceeds from this diagnosis. The acupuncturist, recognizing that the variations of the disease are a consequence of the constitution and temperament, will regularize the energy in the appropriate meridians. The acupuncture needles will be inserted into meridian points that are different from one subject to another, even though the general disease process, in this case colitis, is the same.

This reasoning is equally valid for hypertension. An individual of any temperament may suffer from arterial hypertension, but each particular temperament predisposes the person to one form of hypertension more than another. Recent investigations in cardiology indicate that different behavioral types are associated with different forms of hypertension. This conclusion could be verified by a study of the Chinese temperaments, or more simply of characterology, relative to hypertension.

151

By extension, the reasoning applied to cases of colitis and hypertension can be applied to all forms of disease: asthma, migraine headaches, painful menstruation, etc. This relationship is conveyed in the expression, "Tell me who you are and I will tell you from what you suffer; tell me from what you suffer and I will tell you who you are."

Finally, this approach to disease can be applied to mental problems and psychosomatic disorders as well, by relating them to particular behavioral disturbances. The five essential behaviors in man — anger, joy, reason, sadness, and fear — which were compared in a previous discussion to the general emotions defined by MacLean (25), are related by reciprocal interactions. Therapy is based on this reciprocity. Again, as pointed out earlier in reference to a passage from the *Nei Jing*, anger dominates reason, reason dominates fear, fear dominates joy, joy dominates sadness, sadness dominates anger (and excessive enthusiasm). By treating the appropriate five element points of the various meridians, the acupuncturist can influence behavioral problems. This is not the only effect that acupuncture therapy may have on psychology. In fact, acupuncture is a medical therapy that is rich in techniques to apprehend the most profound psychosomatic illness and mental dysfunction.

Chapter 10

Relevance for the Psychologist

Critical Analysis of the Berger Test

Due to the complexity of an individual's character, several remarks on the value of the Berger test are appropriate. I will not discuss the secondary tests, which explore the breadth of the field of consciousness, including: polarity, the senses, intellectual capabilities, etc. Although these tests are interesting complements to tests of the three primary factors of activity, emotivity, and resonance, they have in my opinion only marginal value for an appreciation of character, the psychobiologic temperament, and the pathology of individuals. It is the three primary factors, through the eight elementary character types that they define, that are instrumental in delineating the eight psychosomatic profiles of the temperaments.

Nonetheless, Berger himself recognized certain shortcomings in the application of his test, for he found that at least 25% of the character types defined by the test scores did not correspond to those either claimed by the subjects or objectively determined.[22] We have verified this figure in our own studies (18). Fifty-eight out of sixty subjects who chose a single character type as most accurately describing themselves can be seen to match the results of the test. By contrast, only 35 out of 73 who chose two or three character types as appropriately describing themselves showed a correspondence with one of the types determined by the test, and the remaining 38 showed no correspondence.

The Berger test thus reflects a certain subjective self-determination. This is verified by the scores given by the experimenter in 95 out of 133 cases (69.9%). In the remaining cases (30.1%), the test was false. This number is close to, although slightly higher than, the scores obtained by Berger.

Berger also failed to note that although the test defines the dominant character type, another character type, sometimes equal in importance, remains unrevealed. In our study the number of these cases was 35 (26.3%). The test was certainly reliable in detecting a character type that existed singly in an individual (43.6%), but only reliable for detecting one part of the complex character in 26.3% of the subjects. The claim that the test is 69.9% reliable should be regarded as relative.

Why does the Berger test result in false determinations? It is not so much that the values given the questions are poor, or that the questions are imprecise, as much as it is that one or two of the primary factors of emotivity, activity, and resonance are often variable in the subjects. Justifiably, when the factors are contradictory, the subjects oscillate between two character types. Frequently, the score on the ten questions regarding one or two of these factors, instead of being clearly high or clearly low, falls near the middle — about 50 from a total of 100. The raw scores do not take into account this oscillation.

For example, let us consider a subject whose character type is simultaneously enthusiastic and sentimental, Shao Yang—Shao Yin. In the test this individual has a score of 75 for emotivity, 56 for activity, and 52 for resonance. The person is thus emotive, active, and secondary; the resulting designation is passionate. However, the structure of this character type does not correspond at all to passionate, but to enthusiastic and sentimental. And, it is the same with both the morphology and pathology.

The psychologist Gex recognized the difficulty in the Berger test and created an alternative, rapid character test of 38 questions. Nonetheless, our experience with this test, excellent in principle, suggested that certain questions were imprecise and ambiguous in regard to several characters.

Other aspects, drawn from personal observations by Berger, have been lauded, but we do not share an equal conviction. For example, we do not agree with Berger and Gex that morbid and macabre are character traits of the nervous type. These are traits that have been assumed too hastily, based perhaps on the works of Baudelaire and Poe. Such traits are far from systematically characteristic of the nervous type.

It is because of these problems that we have modified the Gex test in an attempt to perfect it. Presently, the reliability of the test appears to be greater than 80% for designation of the first three character types, the most important.

At present the test has virtually no application in modern psychology because of its relative inexactitude. This inexactitude, however, should not be used as an indictment of the character types described by Berger. Certainly, tests such as the Minnesota multiphasic test yield more precise and accurate appraisals of the personality, but the diverse descriptions of the personality that result from such tests (hysteric, depressive, etc.), reflect the character types of Berger just as he defined them.

Psychosomatics and Depth Psychology

It was Heinroth who, in 1818, first introduced "psychosomatic" to professional language. The term was later adopted by Delay who, in 1946, introduced psychosomatics in France. It is a field that has interested medical researchers as much as psychologists. Historically, Groddeck can be said to be the founder of psychosomatics. The movement extended from Europe to the United States, mainly as a result of the works of English, Engels, Alexander, and others (35).

The definition of temperaments that has been put forth by acupuncture, where a certain character type subtends a physiological disposition that determines the morbid susceptibilities of that temperament, physical as well as mental, is a definition that closely coincides with the concepts of the American school, and particularly the concepts of Alexander, leader of the school from

1930-1950. He wrote, "Psychologic and somatic phenomena unfold in the same organism; they are but two aspects of the same process" (1). This statement could not better reflect the concept of psychosomatics according to acupuncture. The author adds, "The aims of psychologic and physiologic studies do not essentially differ; what distinguishes the two is their approach."

Since the beginning of Chinese medicine, Chinese physicians have approached physiology and psychologic phenomena with the view that the two are not fundamentally different. For the Chinese, the process common to the two is energetic. The transformations that energy creates on the biologic level parallel those that we observe on the psychologic level, and vice versa: "a repletion of energy in the liver makes the person irascible; excessive anger disturbs the liver."

J. Delay, in 1961, conceived psychosomatics in the sense of terrain, which is as common to Greek medicine as it is to Chinese. He noted that:

> . . . the psychosomatic movement seeks to go beyond organic medicine, which has become more and more specialized in its pursuit of a general form of medicine. The psychosomatic physician places the role of the terrain in the forefront, and thus continues the Hippocratic tradition in medicine. It is a tradition that considers illness less as an imposition of a process extrinsic to the sick person than as a development intimately linked to the nature of the person's reactions and certainly to the nature of the person (13).

This statement coincides remarkably well with the Chinese conception of psychosomatics.

Other approaches approximate the Chinese view. We have already discussed the character profiles of Berger and their relationship to the six Chinese temperaments. There are others, such as the endocrinological typology of Pende, and the embryonic typology of Sheldon. Even the concepts of Alexander on "autonomic neuroses" can be seen to relate to the Chinese model of constitutions. For him there are two types of somatic response to emotional states. First, problems arise in the sympathetic system when the expression of hostile and aggressive tendencies is blocked. Second, problems arise in the parasympathetic system when the tendency to dependence and the search for support is blocked (1).

This view corresponds to that of the temperaments. The Shao Yang and Jue Yin temperaments, with the resonance of their sympathetic nature, have the shen of wood as their CNS substance, expressed by the hun in terms of extroversion and aggressivity. The Tai Yang and Shao Yin temperaments have the shen of water as their CNS substance. This relates to the zhi, will power, and is expressed by fear commanding the adrenal gland to react by fight or flight.

Resonance of a parasympathetic nature in the Tai Yin and Yang Ming temperaments is determined by four characters and is related to yi, the CNS substance of earth governing ideation, and po, the CNS substance of metal governing interiorization of sensory messages. We will see later that dependence and search for support is brought on by a disturbance of these two shen.

Alexander, viewing autonomic neuroses as merely neuroses with accompanying neurophysiologic phenomena, regarded such neuroses as senseless, and expressed his mechanistic and schematic views summarily by describing the psychosomatic symptom as nonsense. On the contrary, the psychoanalytic concepts of Freud give much credence to such symptoms, regarding them as coded messages from the unconscious. They have meaning, meaning in relation to an earlier period in the person's life. Or, in a wider sense, they have meaning as symbols in the universal sense, as has been studied extensively by Jung.

Freud also discovered in his study of neuroses a certain complacency or "somatic obligingness." This is an apparent choice made by the mental state for an organ or bodily function where the conversion of the mental disturbance to the body occurs. This conversion often conveys the intention and significance of the symptom.

If we consider the acupuncture model in relation to the concepts of Freud and Alexander, far from being opposed, there is considerable correspondence. It is true that the structure of a particular character type corresponds to a particular physiologic basis, and this correspondence underlies the affinity of a character type for a specific target organ. Further, the mental state is regarded as capable of determining the physiologic state, structuring and destructuring it, because mental disturbances can disturb the harmonious functioning of the organs.

Chinese medical psychology also agrees with much of psychoanalysis. Initially, Berger associated certain character types with certain morbid personalities, terms intended to convey the concept of mental structures predisposing psychological problems of a similar nature. We now see that the character structure of the enthusiastic (Shao Yang) closely coincides with the phobic personality and anguish neurosis; and that the nervous type (Jue Yin) coincides with the phobic personality as well as the hysterical. The passionate type (Tai Yang) closely coincides with the paranoid personality. The character structure of the sentimental type (Shao Yin) approximates the obsessional and melancholic personality; that of the sanguine type (Yang Ming-earth) the maniacal personality; that of the apathetic type (Tai Yin-metal) the perverse or schizoid personality; that of the amorphous type (Tai Yin-earth) the psychopathic personality; and, finally, the phlegmatic type (Yang Ming-metal) with morbid rationalism (14).

In our discussion of pathology the various mechanisms that underlie disturbances in the meridians were shown with the associated mental disturbances. An example was a disequilibrium between the meridians and the functions of the pancreas and kidney. The disequilibrium was viewed as a consequence of the earth-water relationship, exemplified by the alternating play of domination and reaction (earth encroaches on water, and in reaction water turns back against earth), the bipolar nature of manic-depressive psychosis.

The points of similarity between the Chinese system and the character types of Berger provide indirect evidence for the claim that the Berger system describes "normal" psychiatric profiles. Yet, the specific problems to which such personalities are predisposed — such as the disordering of functions corresponding to the temperaments and reflected in the personality — are explained more completely by acupuncture. This is because there is the implication of constitution in the idea of temperament, connecting the physiology to the character type and therefore to personality and psychological problems.[23]

The principles of Chinese medicine do not exclude the interpretations of psychoanalysis. Psychosomatic and psychoanalytic theories can be reconciled, especially when viewed in the light of the Shen, the CNS substances. One learns, for example, that the yi, the shen of ideation that is connected to the pancreas and to earth, determines both bulimic tendencies and the sensation of emptiness in the head that is often associated with anger, or the panting that is associated with hypoglycemia. One can readily associate yi with orality, and, in the oral stage of Freudian theory, with fixation at this stage and its consequences for the personality.

On the somatic level, however, the yi is related to the endocrine and exocrine pancreas, and to the hypothalamus (33). The relationship with the hypothalamus is especially true in the correspondence of the earth constitution with Diathesis V in diathetic medicine. Menetrier called this a pituitary-pancreatic or pituitary-gonadal disadaptation.

With this in mind it is understandable why amorphous individuals of earth constitution frequently are described as immature or as having a childlike mentality. The lack of ambition that is also common in these individuals often is expressed as a refusal to accept responsibility — in other words, refusal to become an adult. Physiologically there is also a delay of puberty, with absence or irregularity in menstruation among females and possible cryptorchidism (non-descent of testicles) in males, as well as a predisposition to enuresis.

For such people food and sleep are a refuge. They have a pronounced taste for sweets and milk products. They are also disinclined to be tidy. Like their retarded sexuality, this too can be understood either as physiology or as symptomatic of regression on the psychological level.

Another example of the reconciliation between modern psychoanalytic theory and constitution is the notion of po, the substance governing neurosensorial activity, the sensorial messages coming from the exterior. This activity is associated with the lung, to respiration, and to the colon. "The po enters by respiration and leaves through the anus," it is said in the *Nei Jing*. The corresponding behavior can be linked to the anal stage of psychoanalytic theory (33). The corresponding character type is apathetic, economical — expressed in excess as avarice. Somatic problems include constipation, chronic asthma, skin diseases. Conflicts with parental authority or someone symbolizing the parent are frequent, and lead to anorexia.

The anal stage is termed anal-sadistic by Freud. If one explores the psychiatric implications of certain acupuncture points related to the lung and large intestine, one discovers that "the seventh point of the lung meridian, *lieque*, and the associated fifth point of the large intestine, *yangxi*, are the points for treatment of 'raging madness'." Likewise, the tonification point of the lung, *tai yuan* (LU-9) is indicated, in a text written in the middle ages, as the treatment point for "wickedness, hatred, the impulse to speak evil of others, and to say wounding things" (33). Similarly, the dorsal point, *feishu* (BL-3), is the point that has special action on the lung and is the point for the treatment of aggressivity turned toward oneself, with intentions or ideas of suicide. By contrast, the point *shenzhu* (GB-12), situated at the same height as *feishu* (BL-3), on the *du mai* meridian, and directly connected to the cerebrospinal axis and the mental state, is indicated for treatment of evil disposition: "Detest men like fire, desire to kill."[24]

Further study of the classical texts indicates that the Chinese had some understanding of the unconscious. This is particularly the case in relation to po. The meaning of "vegetative spirit" is close to the Freudian "id." In a general sense the Freudian structure of the unconscious is similar to the Chinese Shen. But, again, in the Oriental mind, the biologic is not to be considered separate from the psychologic. (This interrelationship was not unknown to Freud, as can be seen in a number of his works.) We will develop later the deeper meaning of Shen, and how their similarities and differences can be explored in a psychoanalytic context.

Returning to our previous example, the yi and po determine the two temperaments Tai Yin and Yang Ming, which are related to the four non-emotive character types of sanguine, amorphous, phlegmatic, and apathetic. These types can be overlapping, as are the earth and metal constitutions through the Tai Yin and Yang

Ming meridians that connect them. These particular connections underlie the fixations at oral or anal stages that are associated with these temperaments.

All other character types are the emotive ones: enthusiastic, nervous, passionate, and sentimental. In these types the hun and zhi are present, and are joined to emotional susceptibilities related to the orthosympathetic nervous system. This in turn is related to the pericardium and heart meridians, the element fire, and also shen, the vegetative spirit of the heart.

In the Chinese temperaments that correspond to these emotive types — Shao Yang, Jue Yin, Tai Yang, and Shao Yin — the psychosomatic diseases that occur in association with them are not, in the view of Alexander, the result of parasympathetic adaptation to surroundings, but the result of orthosympathetic preparation for action, especially excesses and inhibitions linked to aggressivity. The psychophysiological predisposition that is linked to this aggressivity creates morbid changes in the personality. They are apparently connected to a libidinal investment in the Oedipus complex.

Individuals of these four emotive temperaments, being of sympathetic reactivity and exhibiting behavior centered on aggressivity, have a natural penchant for the carnivorous instinct, for animal meat, the product of the hunt. On a more general and cultural level these types are expressed as the opposition between sedentary and nomadic peoples.

An in-depth study of the Shen permits one to go still further in the understanding of individuals, beyond the psychosomatic and psychoanalytic dimensions of human beings. In effect it opens a metaphysical view of humankind, placing us not only in a cultural, hereditary, and personal context, but also in a harmonious universal and cosmic framework.

The psychosomatic and psychoanalytic approach corresponds to only the electronic and psychosomatic views of acupuncture. The third model, the cosmic model, involves another dimension that cannot be measured without placing acupuncture and Chinese medicine in the philosophic and metaphysical context of their origin. These concepts are the most subtle meanings of Shen.

Because of the complexity of this subject, the discussion of Shen will not be developed extensively. It is better considered in works devoted to philosophy and acupuncture. For the moment, however, we will make the tentative conclusion that the psychosomatic model of acupuncture, the concept of terrain and temperament predisposing to physical and psychological problems, in combination with Shen, can be reconciled with the medical theories of psychosomatics and the symbolic interpretations of psychoanalysis.

The influences on the structure of character are primarily two, according to acupuncture: the parental influence and the terrain. This relativist view permits the reconciliation of the extreme positions taken by the psychoanalysts and the geneticists. It allows the physician to propose psychotherapy for the treatment of an asthmatic and prescribe medication for a neurotic during a program of analysis.

Acupuncture is not the only Chinese method for correction of a disturbance in the terrains. Other methods exist, in particular the utilization of the trace elements. Thus, for example, in various individuals of water constitution, some will be treated by acupuncture, some by treatment with the trace elements copper-gold-silver, and in others by analysis.

It is possible to act directly on the Shen. Again, there are five special, bilaterally located acupuncture points on a meridian on the back that permit the acupuncturist, by needling or by massage, to affect directly the five corresponding shen. Experience has shown that these points must be manipulated with caution, because their stimulation can initiate a sudden mental unblocking or release of the corresponding shen. This clinical observation, verified many times by many practitioners, not only indicates a certain prudence in treatment involving these points, but also indicates that the effect of acupuncture is beyond autosuggestion or imagination.

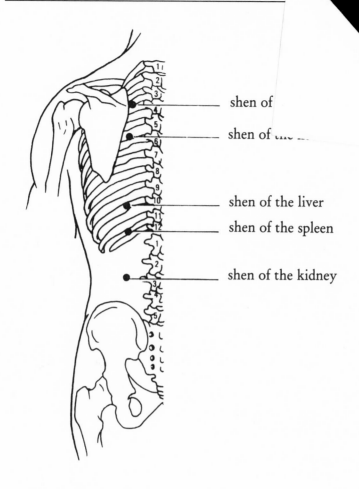

shen of

shen of the

shen of the liver

shen of the spleen

shen of the kidney

Figure 14: The five shen points

By stimulating these places in the body one allows the person to trace moments in the past and in the future. In this sense one can compare the energetic approach of acupuncture with that of certain relaxation methods from yoga, as well as the approach of Wilhelm Reich, especially the bioenergetic and psychotherapeutic behavioral approach.

Chapter 11

Relevance for the Physician

The model of humankind proposed by acupuncture is three-fold: electronic, cosmic, and psychosomatic. In this discussion we will concentrate on the electronic and psychosomatic aspects. Both of these models are internally and externally consistent. That is, not only is the logic of acupunctural diagnosis and treatment regular and predictable, but there are also correlations to Western research and knowledge that are remarkable.

The Electronic Model

This model views humans as a system of discrete polarizations. Phenomena are divisible into left and right, posterior and anterior, upper and lower, internal and external, into hierarchical yin and yang functions, and into relationships among one another, including complementary associations in pairs. Disease is a disturbance of the normal equilibrium of these polarizations. Chinese diagnosis is a consideration of the energetic systems of the body, and follows eight traditional parameters: top and bottom, exterior and interior, hot and cold, yin and yang.

The aim of these categories is to direct the physician to an evaluation of the general disequilibrium and a treatment that will correct this disequilibrium. If, for example, there is a symptom at the top of the body, the physician will automatically assume that there is a loss of harmony between the upper and lower parts. The same reasoning exists for the right and left sides, the interior and exterior. If a symptom is of a yang nature, manifested by a sharp, localized, and precise pain, or else accompanied by a superficial or internal vasodilatation with production of excessive heat, or if the symptom suggests excessive activity or vitality, the part of the body where this symptom exteriorizes has, in effect, captured a bodily energy to the detriment of its opposite. For example, if there is a repletion of yang in the upper part of the body there will be a corresponding insufficiency of yang, and therefore a repletion of yin, in the lower part of the body.

The therapeutics that are associated with acupuncture are a direct result of this reasoning. The acupuncturist, with a view towards reasserting the proper equilibrium, will treat the opposite side to reduce the disequilibrium. The physician will prick a point in the lower body to ameliorate a symptom expressed in the upper body, or needle a point on the left side for a right-sided problem (for example, the left calf for a right-sided sciatica).

Relationships to Physical Phenomena

The sometimes spectacular effects of these therapeutic gestures naturally leads to the question: what are the physical phenomena at work in the meridians whose alteration provokes symptomatic problems? Similarly, what diagnosis, in terms of polarity, accounts for the multiple morbid associations encountered in the same patient?

To take a previous example by way of illustration, an insufficiency of yin of the liver produces a repletion of yang that, along the meridian, has a tendency to ascend, to escape through excess to the top of the chest or toward the brain. The symptoms arising are racing of the heart or migraines. The patient with this disequilibrium is subject to viral or allergic conjunctivitis or to allergic rhinitis, signs related to an overabundance of yang in the liver.

The overabundance of yang in the upper body produces a complementary and antagonistic overabundance of yin in the lower body. With this overabundant yin in the lower body, the energy will not ascend the meridian properly. This engenders varices, hemorrhoids, and pelvic pains. The liver meridian, in the failure of its energy to circulate along its ascending paths, produces a failure of the venous circulation.

These syndromes are associated in various degrees with a disequilibrium of a single meridian, the Jue Yin (the liver meridian connected to the pericardium meridian). This meridian links the lower and upper parts of the body. As already discussed, Jue Yin is also the name of the temperament associated with this constitution, and is the nervous character type: emotive, non-active and primary.[25]

Another example is that of a plethoric subject with a ruddy complexion. One or more arteriosclerotic syndromes are present: headache due to arterial hypertension, hemorrhage of the vitreous of the eye, chest angina, hiatal hernia, arteritis of the lower limbs. In terms of disposition, the person is usually jovial, even exalted on occasion.

In acupuncture this combination of traits suggests that the person suffers from a repletion of yang in the upper part of the body, mainly the chest and head regions. Disequilibrium exists in the Yang Ming meridian, the meridian that is associated with the large arterial branches. The top of the body is primarily yang, vasodilated, red, hot. The lower body is therefore yin, vasoconstricted, white, cold, or even icy if there is arteritis. The therapeutic protocol for this configuration consists of needling those points that reduce the overabundant energy on top and direct it to circulate downward, thereby balancing the two regions. This approach liberates that part of the energy that has a tendency to ascend via the counterflow mechanism in the Yang Ming meridian, and thus obliges it to follow the normal anastomotic path of the meridian.

The identification of the affected meridian is based on association with symptoms. These are associations readily recognized during a course of study in Chinese medicine. The diagnosis is usually confirmed by the traditional taking of pulses at the wrist, a method consisting of palpating the radial artery on each side near the hand with three fingers. The acupuncturist feels, either by strongly pressing his fingers, or, on the contrary, by hardly pressing at all, the circulation of the blood. This maneuver is geared to making twelve impressions, six on the left (three fingers pressed hard, three lightly), and six on the right:

167

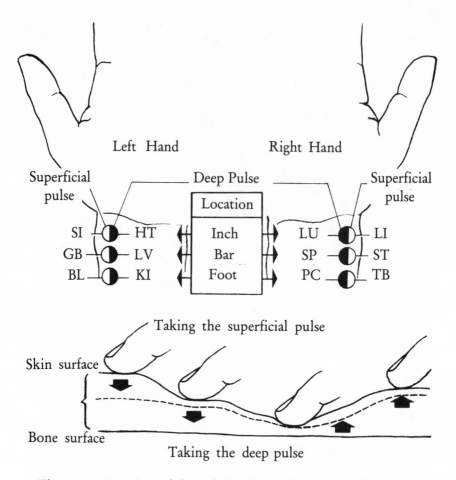

Figure 15: Location of the radial pulses and position of the fingers for palpation

These twelve impressions reflect the health of the individual, and correspond to the degree of repletion or depletion of yang or yin for each of the twelve functions defined by acupuncture. These twelve pulses, however, exist in a left or right polarization, deep or superficial. Additional hierarchical considerations include high (close to the thumb) or low (toward the elbow), exterior or interior, yin or yang:

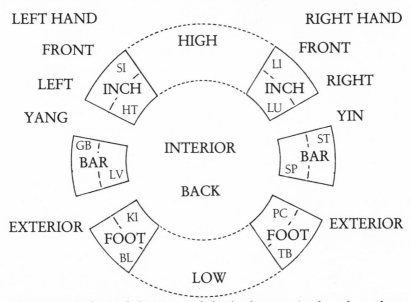

LEFT HAND ... RIGHT HAND

FRONT ... HIGH ... FRONT

LEFT ... RIGHT

YANG ... YIN

INTERIOR

BACK

EXTERIOR ... EXTERIOR

LOW

SI / INCH / HT

LI / INCH / LU

GB / BAR / LV

ST / BAR / SP

KI / FOOT / BL

PC / FOOT / TB

Figure 16: Polarized divisions of the body perceived at the pulses in their anatomic position

Normally, the finger that should feel the pulse (under the pad of the finger) is the middle finger placed on the right wrist, where one can determine the activity of the stomach in relation to the large vessels, a function of the lower Yang Ming (stomach) meridian.[26]

Another characteristic feature of Chinese diagnosis is a consideration of the complexion. The reddish face color of the plethoric individual used above as an example, is a warning sign.

When the meridian under attack has been determined, and one knows the nature of the disorder, it is next necessary to determine, which side of the body is involved. In the case mentioned above for example, the acupuncturist would seek to determine whether it is the left or the right Yang Ming meridian that has a repletion of yang.

The theories of acupuncture denote other pulses that are specific to each function. The Yang Ming meridian has a close relationship with the arterial circulation, and the pulses for the stomach function (zu yang ming) are, for the top of the body, located on the carotid artery, and, for the lower part of the body, on the artery at the dorsal side of the foot, the dorsalis pedis artery. These two regions also correspond to two acupuncture points, *renying* (ST-9), located perpendicular to the carotid artery at the level of the receptors of arterial tension regulation (carotid baroreceptors), and *chang yang* (ST-42) on the dorsalis pedis artery. (The term *chang yang* means "assault on the yang.")

The individual described above, having a repletion of yang in the Yang Ming meridian, is prone to overload and risks hemiplegia if the attack is sufficiently great. The expression "stroke" describes exactly such a consequence in this meridian. Arteritis is also a potential consequence due to a diminution of the arterial circulation in the legs. This is recognized in Western medicine by the disappearance of the pulse in the dorsal artery of the foot.

Thus, according to the tenets of acupuncture, one can determine the disturbed function, the attacked meridian, the global disequilibrium of energy between the upper and lower, deep and superficial levels of the body, and, through a consideration of the pulses, even the threatened side. It is this that will determine the tactics of treatment. The acupuncturist will regularize the affected side and use the unaffected side for the reequilibration, (i.e., needling the points on the side opposite to the disturbed side).

The arterial hypertension that afflicts the subject in this example is most likely due to increased peripheral resistance — the resistance in the vessels. The Yang Ming meridian accompanies arterial circulation. The relationship does not stop here, however. Normally, the energy in the Yang Ming meridian circulates centrifugally from the head to the feet. There is also an energy circulating as a countercurrent and it is this energy that provokes arterial hypertension by increasing vascular resistance.

In addition to the rong energy — the essential, endocrine jing energy — and the Shen — the CNS substances — there is also the *wei* energy. According to the first acupuncture text this wei energy is the "offspring" of the stomach meridian. The *Nei Jing* describes it as "defensive, warlike and fierce." It is associated with thermoregulation, vasoconstriction, and the immune defenses of the body. The wei energy also accounts for two-thirds of the strength of the pulse, that is, the resistance of the vessels. This energy is considered yang, in contrast to the nourishing rong energy, which is yin. When the stomach meridian has an overabundance of yang, this wei energy is in repletion. Warlike and fierce, it ascends to the top of the body via the Yang Ming meridian instead of circulating centrifugally from the head to the feet. This is the yang assault, the attack of hypertension that can lead to chest angina or stroke. Here the person is plethoric, or at the least has a reddish complexion, verifying the overabundance of yang in the top part of the body.

In the opposite condition, an insufficiency of the wei energy, the person is pale, suffers from a loss of appetite and so becomes thin, is sensitive to the cold, depressed, and melancholic (in the psychiatric sense of that term). Infections are common, for there are immune problems. Cancer of the stomach is a possibility. The emptiness of energy in the stomach is, as mentioned earlier, associated with an insufficiency in the spleen, and is thus manifested as an insufficiency of T and B lymphocytes. When the wei energy of the stomach is exhausted there is no more skin color. The skin is waxy and there is no pulse. The vascular system collapses; tension in the vessels no longer exists.

This example illustrates again the interrelationships that exist between functions. In acupuncture, when one explores physiological consequences, multiple systems are involved. In our example it was necessary to consider the immune system, the maintenance of vascular tension, digestion and appetite, all as a consequence of a disturbance of the stomach meridian.

Relationships to Physiology

We have attempted elsewhere to put forth hypotheses on the possible physiologic connections between processes described separately in standard Western physiology (33). It is possible, for example, that the secretion of hydrochloric acid by the parietal cells in the mucosal lining of the stomach is dependent on the secretion of gastrin from secretory cells in the pylorus, which are themselves dependent on the secretion of histamine from the mast cells. It is the mast cells and not the acid-producing parietal cells that respond to stimulation of the parasympathetic innervation of the stomach. Mast cells, however, also are important in the defense system of the organism, and they are found not only in the stomach but also in the connective tissue and blood where they circulate in the form of polymorphonuclear basophils. One can thus see the relationship, at least on this cellular level, that exists between defense and digestion. The same relationship probably exists between digestion and vascular resistance, and between vascular resistance and defense.

Investigators are presently making inquiries into the role of gastrin, secreted by the stomach and found circulating in the blood vessels. It is possible that the gastrin present in the brain is associated with certain extremes of mood, like gaiety and laughter — the temperament usually associated with repletion of yang of the stomach. It may be a mediator of endocrine regulation of the hypothalamus through the link that the latter has with the stomach, pancreas, and spleen. These organs are the conjoined viscera of the earth constitution, and the hypothalamic disadaptation described by Menetrier.

Relationship to Genetics

A study of the contributions of genetics in the determination of the terrain, as well as for the character type and the whole set of individual biologic processes, will undoubtedly shed further light on the relationships proposed by acupuncture. Immunology, which is linked to genetics by the expression of certain antigens (like the HLA system), should provide complementary support. The relationships yet to be validated by scientific investigation are already a part of the physiologic model put forth by acupuncture, and are the basis for much of its system of therapeutics.

The relationships yet to be demonstrated in the West already exist in the acupunctural physiologic model, and therapy by acupuncture or even the prescription of antigens or tissue antibodies, provides convincing evidence that this is so. One can needle the point *renying* (ST-9), the carotid point that the Chinese call "window of the sky" because it is like a safety valve that protects the cephalic region. Acupuncture at this point should be undertaken with caution, because one can also prick the point *chang yang* (ST-42), the "assault on the yang," to disperse this energy with the same aim. This therapy can also take advantage of the complementary influence of antigenic activity, for there already exist numerous preparations of antigens or antibodies from specific organs, which act in infinitesimally small doses, and whose action is certain. Cardiologists no doubt will be surprised if researchers one day succeed in demonstrating that diluted extracts of gastric mucus ameliorate certain types of hypertension.

The results of initial investigations are encouraging, although these methods have generally remained, for at least the last thirty years, distant from hospital trials. The few that have taken place in France have demonstrated convincingly the efficacy of the acupuncture method of treating arteritis of the lower limbs by promoting collateral circulation.

The Psychosomatic Model

We have shown how the model proposed by acupuncture is enriched by the categorization of constitutions and temperaments, especially in conjunction with the character types defined by Berger. In combination with the relationships that can be drawn between the twelve organic functions defined by acupuncture and the diatheses of Menetrier, one can conceive the temperaments and therefore the biologic terrains in the following hierarchic fashion.

Emotivity

Emotivity is subordinate to physiology, and is subordinate in the sense that it appears to be linked to the autonomic nervous system. A constitutional tendency to excitation of the orthosympathetic system makes emotive persons sympathicotonic; the sympathetic nervous system dominates, to a greater or lesser degree, the general functioning of the body organs. Contrarily, nonemotivity is linked to a predominant excitation of the parasympathetic system, to dominance of the general functioning of the body organs by the parasympathetic nervous system — a constitutional parasympathicotony, or at least a parasympathetic sensitivity. The antagonistic roles that exist between these two systems remain to be defined in relation to the limbic (autonomic) system, the incontestable seat of emotive experience.

Activity

Apparently linked by antagonistic relationships with the muscular system and the system of defense and metabolism (the reticuloendothelial system), activity is determined by the strength or weakness of the muscular system and, to a lesser degree, by the

173

hypometabolism of the reticuloendothelial system. Conversely, inactivity is predicted by either hypermetabolism of the reticuloendothelial system or by asthenia or inhibition of the muscular system. These two systems appear therefore to be related antagonistically. This relationship is similar to the relationship that exists between the temperaments described by Galen, in which the bilious type is opposed to the phlegmatic. It is also similar to the relationship that exists between the muscular and digestive systems, which is claimed in the classification of Sigaud.

This antagonism may also reflect the oxidation-reduction (redox) reactions of metabolism. The more primitive system sprang from pure anaerobic metabolism, and is characteristic of fermentive or glycolytic cells in the reticuloendothelial system. Similar to bacteria, these cells have the capacity to phagocytize material that is foreign to the organism. These cells are part of the defense system of the body. The relationship that exists between immunity and the entire lymphatic system is expressed in characterology in terms of phlegmatic or lymphatic. The other metabolic pathway, the more recent, consumes oxygen and is associated with the locomotor system. In characterology, this type of metabolism is associated with the muscular or bilious type.

In summary, the biological basis for the activity factor in characterology seems to be related to general redox processes, removal and transferral of electrons from an oxidizing atom to an atom thus reduced. Those persons who have a greater tendency toward the aerobic pathway have a great faculty for action, which is mediated by a predominance of the muscular system and inhibition of the reticuloendothelial system. Those persons oriented toward the anaerobic pathway are characterized by inactivity, which is mediated by a predominance of the reticuloendothelial system and inhibition of the muscular system.

Resonance

This factor appears to be linked clearly to the functions of the central nervous system, especially the lemniscal (fibrous) and extralemniscal pathways. Resonance in terms of constitution and characterology can be described as follows: primarity is a constitution preferentially active in the direct lemniscal pathway of the central nervous system. This pathway is the one carrying the reflex arc. From the second neuron in the paramedullary sympathetic ganglion the path ascends the spinal cord to the superior neural centers and makes contact through synaptic junctions with the great pyramidal cells of the fifth layer of the cortex. These cells, once stimulated, direct the influx to the periphery by the pyramidal pathway, the path that drives the muscular system during locomotion, and mediates the fight or flight response. This is equivalent to the short-circuit action described by Corman, the primary movement that defines both the physical and mental behavior of the primary subject. The tendency to primarity corresponds to preserving what Laborit calls "generalized homeostasis" (21).

The constitution characterized by preferential activity of the indirect extralemniscal pathway is termed secondarity. An offspring of the direct pathway, it gives rise to collaterals at the level of the cerebral trunk, which make contact through synapses with the multisynaptic neurons of the reticular formation. From here connection is made with the cortex by two distinct routes, one that passes through the internal capsule and terminates in the superficial layers of the cortex, and the other, more complex one, that makes relays with the thalamic nuclei (diffuse thalamic system of Jasper), then travels toward the more focalized nuclei of the thalamus, and finally terminates in the cortex through specific differentiated zones.

This route, as specified by Laborit, is that associated with attention or the capacity to focus on a particular problem. It defines the physical and psychological behavior of the secondary subject. The tendency is called "restrained homeostasis" by Laborit.

Character Types and Hormones

The three fundamental factors of character type — emotivity, activity, and resonance, which, as shown above, can be related to specific physiologic processes, are associated in a variety of combinations to form the eight character types defined by Berger. Likewise, these three factors, their association by twos, the eight possible combinations of the eight characters, each mold the physical form. This molding includes varied and specific morphologic characters as much as the physiognomy, which we have seen in the descriptions put forth by Corman (11).

175

Each character type is subtended by a specific endocrine tendency. This relationship is described below.

The enthusiastic Shao Yang. The individual of this type appears to be hyperthyroid. Emotive, active, and primary, he or she is sympathicotonic, muscular and lemniscal, hyperexcitable. One thus understands why the primary value Berger attributed to this character is action. Free of restraint, this person indulges to the fullest his or her inclination to act and fight, and thus the behavior is one of hyperactivity.

The nervous Jue Yin. The person of this type also appears to be hyperthyroid, but also hypoparathyroid. Emotive, non-active, and primary, he or she is sympathicotonic, of inhibited muscular hyperexcitability, and lemniscal. The inclination to action and fight is replaced by inhibition and flight. The muscular hyperexcitability, rather than being expressed in movement, is expressed in tics and muscle spasms, which can on occasion appear as tetany, and manifestations of a parallel hypoparathyroidism. The flight reflex is expressed in a variety of ways, including jumping at the slightest noise via a lemniscal facilitation, or even symbolically, like flight in dreams or to an assumed personality. For Berger, the dominant value of this type is diversion.

The passionate Tai Yang. The person of this type appears as medullary hyperadrenal and hypergonadal (testosterone or progesterone). Emotive, active, and secondary, he or she is sympathicotonic, extralemniscal, and shows a muscular hyperexcitability. The secretion of hormones associated with the fight response is also associated with factors of the greatest activity and integration through the predominance of extralemniscal activity. From the latter come great intellectual feats, including memorization. For Berger, the dominant value of this character type is the goal, the ideal to be accomplished.

The sentimental Shao Yin. The person of this type appears as cortical hypoadrenal and hypogonadal. Emotive, non-active, and secondary, he or she is insufficiently sympathetic, extralemniscal, and shows an inhibition of the muscular system. The hormonal profile predisposes to the flight reaction, but also to being startled into paralysis as a result of muscular inhibition combined with the extralemniscal predominance. Sympathetic insufficiency with erratic patterns of adrenergic discharge may also be observed. The psychological behavior of this individual appears as a fear of failure, a lack of enterprise, and a defeatist spirit. Yet at the same time this behavior is balanced by introspection and the veneration of lucidity through refuge in ideal values. For Berger, the dominant value of the sentimental type is intimacy.

The sanguine Yang Ming. The person of this type appears as endocrine hypopancreatic and exocrine hyperpancreatic (the digestive classification of Sigaud). Non-emotive, active, and primary, he or she is an insufficient parasympathetic, shows a hypometabolic pattern in the support tissues (connective tissues and the reticuloendothelial system), and is lemniscal. In terms of behavior this hormonal pattern appears as extraversion and mania, but within normal limits. The sanguine type has initiative and a practical mind, a certain worldly gaiety, and is opportunistic. For Berger, the dominant value of this type is social success.

The amorphous Tai Yin. The person of this type appears as endocrine hyperpancreatic and exocrine hypopancreatic, and sometimes hypothyroid. Non-emotive, non-active, and primary, this type is parasympathicotonic, hypermetabolic in the support tissues (reticuloendothelial system and spleen), and lemniscal. Of the opposite hormonal configuration as the sanguine Yang Ming, this type has hypomaniacal and extroverted tendencies that induce a connective tissue and digestive hypermetabolism. Behaviorally there is an absence of emotional responses, indeed an intellectual one-sidedness that is linked to a parasympathicotonia, which is itself linked to a lemniscal predominance. Of good character, inclined to laziness and little ambition, the amorphous type has a dominant value of pleasure.

The phlegmatic Yang Ming. The person of this type appears as slightly hypothyroid and slightly hyperparathyroid or normocrine. Non-emotive, active, and secondary, this type is insufficiently parasympathetic, hypometabolic of the defense (reticuloendothelial) system, and extralemniscal. The endocrine relationships predispose this person to little emotion. He or she has a characteristic sang-froid, and is capable of objective reflection, exact observation, good judgment, and appropriate action. The dominant value, for Berger, is the law.

177

The apathetic Tai Yin. The person of this type appears as hypothyroid and hyperparathyroid. Non-emotive, non-active, and secondary, this type is parasympathicotonic, is hypermetabolic in the defense (lymphatic) system, and extralemniscal. The endocrine profile, which is identical to the phlegmatic Yang Ming, is associated with lymphatic hypermetabolism, which inhibits action and determines a cold, almost indifferent character that is accentuated by parasympathicotonia. The predominance of the extralemniscal path inclines the person to the most deferred, calculated, and carefully thought-out reaction. Closed, secretive, taciturn and conservative, the apathetic type is difficult to get along with, indifferent to social life, and prefers solitude. The dominant value of the apathetic Tai Yin is tranquillity.

Finally, it is interesting to raise the question of whether the three biologic factors of behavior determine the endocrinological predominance or whether the hormones predetermine the metabolic, autonomic and CNS reactivity. The latter hypothesis does not exclude the former, if oxidative-reductive metabolism is viewed in its most general sense. It is certainly incontestable that the endocrine role (including the role of each hormone in the general metabolism of the body) is associated with the activity and antagonism of the muscular and defense systems that orient in a global fashion the oxidative-reductive metabolism (see also the discussion on temperament and the trace elements further on).

The Role of Education

The role of education also remains to be defined in the development of the character type. Education is capable of acting either in opposition to, or reinforcement of, the genetic determinants.

The Tai Yang temperament could be used as an example of the effects of education on temperament. This type is defined as a constitutional excess of yang in the bladder meridian that runs along the cerebrospinal axis and maintains direct connections with the brain. Through its relationship with the yang aspect of the kidney-adrenal-gonad meridian, one can say that this is the most adrenergic temperament. Experimentally it has been established that the most aggressive strains of rats contain 25% more noradrenalin in their brains than controls (22). The quality of leadership and authority thus has biological support. But psychologic conditioning, through education, is also at play, because observations in man have shown that "individuals born of dominating parents most often become dominant themselves, due to the education they receive" (22).

In my opinion, the son of an authoritative and abusive Tai Yang mother may become an authoritative and abusive Tai Yang individual as a result of the maternal education he will receive, for it is an education based on competitiveness imposed on the genetically determined hyperadrenal character type.

If, on the contrary, the same education is imposed on the individual of amorphous or sentimental character, which is the hypopancreatic or hypoadrenal character, the result will be markedly different. In the first case the education may lead to latent or patent homosexuality, and in the second to extreme inhibition, with functional or psychological impotence.

Temperaments and Functions

The three factors described above are linked to the character and the endocrine types, and, in a cooperative fashion, delimit six distinct temperaments. These six temperaments in turn subtend the character type, the endocrine and organic functions. As we discussed earlier, the Western anatomic-pathologic classification of the body only gives a glimpse of these broader relationships. And yet such relationships do exist, and they arose not from chance or from an Asiatic, esoteric fantasy, but from a knowledge of complex and exact physiologic mechanisms. Proof of this contention can be illustrated in the following example.

The wood constitution is characterized by a vulnerability of the liver and gallbladder meridians, predisposing the individual to endocrine disorders of hyperthyroidism, hypoparathyroidism, and hyperestrogenism. The latter leads to painful menses, as well as pelvic pain, mastosis, migraines, and a predisposition to form fibromas.

In terms of the relationship that exists between the liver and the thyroid gland, Linquette wrote: "The liver appears as an indispensable organ to the biologic activity of thyroid hormones" (24). This conclusion is based mainly on the role of the liver in the

179

transformation of the T4 form of the thyroid hormone to T3, which is the more biologically active form. But the liver is also capable of catabolizing the thyroid hormones by the process of conjugation. Thyroid hormones also act on the liver itself, especially at the level of glycogenesis-glycogenolysis, as well as steroid metabolism.

A relationship also exists between the liver and the parathyroid gland. Hypoparathyroidism is manifested by an insufficient secretion of parathyroid hormone, which leads to hypocalcemia and to neuromuscular hyperexcitability. This leads to attacks of tetany and episodes of muscular spasms, which are frequent among French and Latin women. According to Linquette, it is probable that this hormone is hydrolyzed and therefore inactivated by the liver (24).

The thyroid and parathyroid glands are related in that thyrocalcitonin, a hormone of thyroid origin, acts in an antagonistic fashion against the parathyroid and thus induces hypocalcemia. The sex hormones, mainly estrogen, also have a hypocalcemic action.

Thus, according to Linquette, the relationship that exists between the liver and the parathyroid gland is one that takes place at the muscular level. (The level is a function of the wood constitution and the liver, according to acupuncture.) The muscular level is intimately involved with glycogen and calcium, and with the elements governing their metabolism (24). As for vitamin D, which augments the calcium level, it too is intimately linked to the liver.

In terms of the relationship that exists between the liver and the estrogens, the estrogens are synthesized primarily in the ovary. They require certain proteins as carriers which, as with the thyroid hormones, are synthesized in the liver. The synthesis of estradiol and estrone is dependent on pregnenolone, and this latter compound is synthesized by the liver (and secondarily by the intestine).

The liver is also a target organ of estrogens. In a recent medical article, de Liquires wrote:

It is now certain that the liver is not only the principal center for the catabolism of estrogens but is also their target organ. The hepatocyte contains cytosolic and nuclear receptors that make a cell at least partly estrogen-dependent. The hepatocyte responds by a series of programmed metabolic reactions to the estrogen that it receives prior to inactivating and eliminating it. These estrogen-dependent metabolic responses can result in, besides a slowing of bile excretion (which can favor the formation of stones), synthesis of certain coagulation factors (which can bring on disorders of coagulation), angiotensinogen (which is associated with hypertension), and the VLDL (very low density lipoproteins), proteins that carry triglycerides in the plasma.

We have only just now begun to realize that the negative physiological consequences of taking estrogens for contraception are the result of the effects of estrogens on the liver.

Likewise, it is important to realize that these morbid associations are all a part of Diathesis I as defined by Menetrier. Again, problems of this diathesis could be partially or totally corrected by taking the element manganese. It is useful to recall that Diathesis I corresponds to the liver and gallbladder functions and their respective meridians.

Thus, we see that when one speaks of the liver function in acupuncture it has a broad meaning, much broader than the term does in Western medicine. In the latter case this organ is viewed as primarily an organ of digestion. And even if modern knowledge is amplified by the larger perspective that a knowledge of acupuncture can bring, a certain amount of lag time will occur before Western physicians alter their views. For, as we have shown, the notion of terrain is large, encompassing functional, organic, endocrine, and characterological aspects. Yet it is this broader view that allows one to understand more fully the morbid associations that occur as a consequence of pathology.

Temperaments and Meridians

In acupuncture, each function is linked to and dependent on a meridian. This concept postulates an anatomy different from a material one, as well as autonomous physical phenomena. The exact nature of these phenomena remain to be elucidated precisely; nonetheless, it is postulated that each meridian energizes its function and follows a precise course that links this function to various organic parts. There are relationships established between the organ and anatomic regions or functions seemingly disparate from the organ. These relationships reconcile well with the grouping of pathological entities that have occurred in Western medicine, especially when such groupings are those included in the diathetic approach to medicine.

An example of this is the liver and the venous system through the intermediary of the centripetal meridian of the liver. Another example is the link between the shoulder and the lung meridian, a link that allows acupuncturists to normalize this meridian in cases of inflammation of the shoulder (scapulo-humeral periarthritis). We have seen that this ailment is associated especially with persons of metal constitution, as well as respiratory vulnerability, based on the observations of Menetrier. The appearance of periarthritis has been shown to occur in association with pulmonary tuberculosis. The right or left occurrence of the shoulder inflammation corresponds to the right or left lung attacked by the tuberculosis. The problem thus is directly associated with the affected lung. The same linkage of organ and region can be shown in other situations. There is a greater frequency of migraines on the right side and the scapular pain that is associated with gallbladder stones. The most affected meridian is homolateral to the gallbladder.

The existence of this energetic network is significant for another reason. The meridians are the junction of mind and body. One can influence the other. Disorders of the meridians affect both the biological and psychological activities. Behavioral tendencies can modify the biological ones, and vice versa. To speak of the relationship metaphorically, the meridian is the hyphen in the word psycho-somatic.

To understand completely the role of the meridians in the body, one must consider the relationships that exist between the energy of the meridians and oxidation-reduction. This will be considered in detail shortly. Initially, it is helpful to recall the correspondence between the constitutions and the diatheses described by Menetrier.

Temperaments and Trace Elements

The twelve meridians are in effect grouped by twos to form the six temperaments. These six temperaments are coordinated with the five constitutions by binary regrouping. The five constitutions are superimposable on the five diatheses, and, in the event of disorder, are correctable by a trace element or the precise association of these metallic ions. Their action is catalytic and acts at the most subtle, infra-atomic level to modify the active site of the affected molecule, and renders it operational enough to participate in biochemical reactions.

The entire set of biochemical reactions that occur in the body can be grouped in families according to their sensitivity to one catalyst. Its activity, slowed or perturbed, is expressed by symptoms that can be grouped into patterns. Each pattern, called a diathesis, through its relationship with one of the five elements of acupuncture, places the primary trace element of the diathesis in relation to the corresponding meridian of the energetic network. Thus the catalyst manganese influences the activity of the liver in its true hepatic meaning by correcting symptoms of biliary dyskinesia, dyspeptic problems, as well as allergic problems. These problems correspond to those of energetic phenomena operating in the Jue Yin meridian, the meridian of the liver. Stimulation of this meridian corrects the disorders classified in oligotherapy as a part of Diathesis I (in acupuncture classified as the wood constitution). The associated catalysts, manganese and cobalt, influence the activity of the liver in its extrahepatic meaning by correcting symptoms of hyperthyroidism, venous problems, and hemorrhoids. They also correct the dystonic symptoms of sympathicotonia, which correspond to disorders of energetic phenomena operating in the liver meridian, Jue Yin, on the lower body. They also correct disorders in the extensions of the Jue Yin meridian in the upper body, the pericardium meridian. These disorders are part of Diathesis III that Menetrier called dystonic or, if one prefers, of the wood-fire constitution that represents the overall Jue Yin meridian.

The identity of the disorders that occur in the meridians has in part been aided by the investigations of Menetrier himself. In researching his concept of the diatheses, he carried out a whole series of measurements of blood constants, particularly pH and the electron potentials of pH (rH2), two indices that permit one to evaluate the oxidation-reduction potential of the interior milieu.[27] Menetrier, based on the findings of this research, proposed that the diatheses correspond to different states of oxidation-reduction in the interior milieu. Diathesis I, allergic, corresponding to the metabolism of persons of wood constitution, exhibits an acidic and reduced internal milieu. Diathesis II, hyposthenic, corresponding to persons of metal constitution, has an acidic and oxidized milieu. Diathesis III, dystonic, corresponding to the fire constitution and in a general way to metabolic evolution with aging, has an alkaline and reduced milieu. Diathesis IV, anergic, corresponding to water constitution and to the extreme stages of cellular aging, has an alkaline and oxidized milieu. Diathesis V, disadaptive, corresponding to earth and to a neutral point, is for Menetrier a possible transition state between the four other states.

This hypothesis of Menetrier, which I believe warrants the most serious analysis, constitutes a global approach to biology, beyond specific tissue metabolism. It is a method that categorizes not only the constitutions but the disorders organized around them. This approach also permits one to perceive in synthetic fashion the electromagnetic phenomena that operate in the body, and the oxidation-reduction, like a balance sheet, that underlies the physical phenomena at work in the meridians and which go under the general names of energy and yin-yang.

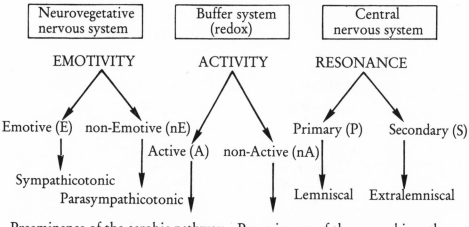

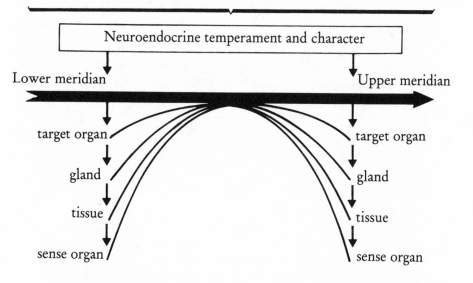

Figure 17: Psychosomatic organization of the meridians

But, according to acupuncture, the environment also is important in the development of the body, as we noted in the opening chapter. In this regard Henriet noted that the environment plays a primordial role in the normal or abnormal evolution of genetic material (6). Professor Magnin, rector of the University of Strasbourg, expressed (at the same conference) that the redox system "was the keystone of biologic harmony, the turntable where the quality of life either is maintained or fails." Cancer, he underlined, "is a disease of regulation" (6). The environment, in its broadest sense, acts in a significant way on the unfolding of the metabolic level of the cell. If the environment proves hostile, the redox equilibrium can be broken, detoxification is insufficient and, at the cellular level, leads to membrane hyperpolarization. Vascular shunts arise and, finally, territorial anoxia.

> The causes of this hostility are varied. Chemical pollution can be responsible, but also specific viruses, the excess or absence of such factors as nutrition, stimulation, rest, cellular detoxification, and psychologic and affective factors. . .

> Quality of life means first of all an ample and vigorous respiration of all of the tissues, and an educated mind, conscious and responsible for its functioning (6).

The principles of health maintenance as taught by Chinese medicine and philosophy, and recorded in the *Nei Jing*, are no different from the conclusions of Professor Magnin. Yet one has still to define with precision the functioning of the brain, both biologically and energetically, and to define the psychophysiologic mechanisms that can act on its functioning to wall off that part of freedom that devolves to the individual. The attempt to further this definition has been the purpose of *Character and Health*.

Chapter 12

Perspectives and Conclusions

Acupuncture proposes electronic, cosmic, and psychosomatic models of the human body. In the psychosomatic model, relationships between medicine and behavioral psychology, as well as depth psychology, can be established. Biological support for each of the models can be obtained, including a genetic basis for character types. The original psychosomatic model proposed by acupuncture is further enriched by its link with the character types of Berger and the diatheses of Menetrier.

The cosmic model of acupuncture places emphasis on the relationship of man to his environment, not only on his immediate ecological milieu but also that of his universe and the planets in which are found the origin of his creation and the bonds that subordinate him to its rhythms.

The electronic model proposes the existence of an energetic anatomy of the body, superimposed on the organic, material one. The energetic form structures the material form. The model is but one ancient Chinese concept that the science of the twentieth century in the West has until now not even suspected.

Acupuncture may thus be viewed as an approach to medicine based on the concept of a terrain, an approach applicable to both prevention and repair. Viewed in combination with Western approaches to psychology, diagnosis and therapy, as well as to

187

biology and the basic sciences, this approach provides a theoretical model that is rich in potential reward.

The synthesis of a more complete model of health and illness could serve as a theoretical model for research into the possible relationship of genetics and morphology, genetics, immunology and terrain, genetics and behavior, genetics and psychiatry, and for relationships in physiology, all of which were until now studied separately. Perhaps more importantly it could also serve as the model from which might evolve suggestions of strategies for more effective maintenance of health and the prevention of disease.

The public seeks in growing numbers the ear and comprehension of the therapist who views the patient in all his or her physical and psychological dimensions. In the last few years we have begun to recognize that even in civilized countries like France and the United States there are critical shortcomings in health maintenance. The losses that are incurred as a consequence of these deficiencies are also critical, for they are both financial and physical. We no longer enjoy the most precious human commodity: good health.

It is to be hoped that the approach to illness taken by Western medicine will not continue to neglect the notion of terrains. Rare, not to say nonexistent, are the times that the student of medicine has been presented seriously with acupuncture, homeopathy, phytotherapy, the trace elements, or even the idea of constitution and temperament outside of psychosomatic medicine. Accuracy in the sciences cannot be achieved without facts supported by a complete comprehension of genetic, immunologic, ecologic, psychologic, and other such integral factors. Yet it is adherence to such accuracy that is the basis and strength of the spirit of research and progress.

Appendix One

Heart — Brain Duality

Are the Occidental and Chinese views on the supremacy of the heart or the brain contradictory? They are not! The brain has complex neuroendocrine metabolisms that scientific study has shown cannot be disputed. Acupuncture deals with an anatomy of the body other than the material anatomy of the organs (the meridians) and a physiology other than metabolic (energy).

Certainly there can be no doubt that from the liver come the syntheses of cholesterol, coagulation factors, proteins, and glycogen. Yet these findings do not obviate the existence of an electromagnetic network that is the meridian system, nor the points on the meridians that can be verified by electrical measurement. The meridian system is like an antenna capturing external influences that are capable of acting on the related organs. Moreover, it is the meridian system that is sensitive to electronic perturbations long before hepatic metabolism is disturbed. And if the organ is ill, if the psychological behavior of the patient is injurious to this organ, the damage or disturbance will be reflected at the surface of the body on the corresponding meridian.

Sophisticated methods of detection already permit us to measure the intensity of these energetic disturbances. With such instrumentation, research can now establish the existence of the bridges between these energetic networks and the material functioning of organs. Chinese, Russian, and American investigators are undertaking such research.

The difference, then, between Western and Chinese views of physiology is a conceptual one. Western physiology is primarily anatomopathologic: it studies cell, tissue, and organ metabolism. Chinese physiology is primarily a study of energy flux in electromagnetic fields. In this view the energetic circuitry is superimposable on metabolism and organic function, yet remains distinct.

Although the brain is regarded as having considerable importance in psychological functions, the heart meridian is regarded to be the energetic center. However, as with the rest of the energetic circuitry, it is distinct from the actual organ and is partially superimposable on it. The primary psychological functions, the Shen or CNS substances, operate in this energetic center of the body. After the Shen reach the brain behavior is expressed. The heart meridian thus acts as a relay station before cerebral expression. By way of analogy, the central position of the heart meridian can be compared to the nucleus of an atom and the meridians to the orbits of electrons revolving about it.

The heart meridian, then, according to acupuncture, is considered to have an organic function, comparable to that recognized by Western medicine, and an energetic function. The brain is energized by the eight particular meridians that convey the jing and by the combination of principal and distinct meridians. The point located on the posterior fontanelle, at the top of the head, *bai hui*, means in Chinese "the hundred meetings," alluding to the fact that all the energetic networks converge at this point.

In terms of the relationship between psychological activity and organ function, a weakness in organs produces a modification in the corresponding psychological behavior. Likewise extreme mental attitudes can provoke changes in the corresponding organic functions. It thus can be seen that acupuncture is truly a psychosomatic medicine, reflecting the psychological, emotional, and organic origin of functional problems. The reader is referred to *Terrains and Pathology in Acupuncture*, for further discussion.

Appendix Two

Cybernetic Organization in Biology

This scheme, illustrated differently, is found in the symbolic and well-known representation of the yin-yang principle, the effector of Tao, called *Tai Qi*. This concept expresses simultaneously the alternation between yin and yang, the transformation from one to the other, and the antagonism between the two.

Figure 18: Tai Qi, the yin-yang principle, effector of Tao.

Yin also is represented symbolically as a discontinuous dash and yang as a continuous dash. The symbol has been considered in detail by Joseph Needham in his article, "Waves and Particles in the Chinese Scientific Thought of Antiquity and the Middle Ages" (31).

Figure 19: Symbols of yin and yang

191

In atomic physics the binary principle of yin-yang encompasses the opposing principles of exclusion described by Pauli (describing a yang principle), and by Carnot-Clausius (describing a yin principle) which involve antagonistic complementarity in the gravitation of electrons. The principle can also be applied to the laws of elementary particles, as Capra has shown in his work, *The Tao of Physics* (8).

Appendix Three

Classification

The system of classification based on elements brings together the organ functions and their meridians into groups other than that proposed for grouping the functions and meridians according to the six energies. In the discussion of the six temperaments the gallbladder (yang) was coupled with the triple burner (yang) to form Shao Yang. In the elemental system of classification, however, the gallbladder is coupled with a yin organ of similar nature or affinity, the liver. Affinity also underlies the selection that occurs in the anastomosis of the twelve meridians at the extremity of the four limbs. For example, the meridian of the gallbladder ends and the meridian of the liver begins; the pericardium meridian ends and the small intestine meridian begins.

The coupling of the liver with the gallbladder is a logical one, likewise that of the kidney and bladder, and the stomach and pancreas. Because the stomach and pancreas play a critical role in the physiology of digestion through the secretion of necessary digestive enzymes, the relationship between the stomach and pancreas is clear. The coupling of the spleen and pancreas, however, appears less obvious.

Modern investigations in embryology have revealed that the tail of the pancreas and the spleen arise from a common bud, and the head of the pancreas and stomach arise from another bud. Also, from the viewpoint of hematology, the stomach secretes the absorption factor by which vitamin B12 is absorbed from food into the blood. This factor is then utilized in the synthesis of red blood cells. The spleen is the site of destruction of old red blood cells. Thus, given the contemporary understanding of the relationships that exist between these organs, the coupling of the spleen and stomach described by the ancient Chinese becomes clearer.

The association of the pericardium meridian and the triple burner meridian is logical because of their correspondence to the orthosympathetic and parasympathetic systems. The association of the heart and the small intestine is justified by the Chinese view of the small intestine acting as a lake that regulates the course of the river (the bloodstream), from which comes its association with the heart, the master of the circulation. As for the pairing of the lung meridian with the large intestine meridian, there is again an embryological commonality that adequately justifies the pairing.

Clinically, the relationship that acupuncture claims to exist between the lung and skin explains the associations seen between respiratory symptoms and cutaneous pathology, such as the association of asthma with cutaneous attacks of eczema.

Once again it appears that the Chinese method of classification is not contradictory to the findings of Occidental medicine. The difference lies primarily in the point of departure. Again, Occidental medicine is primarily organic and materialistic, relying on the study of tissues and physical experimentation; acupuncture is primarily energetic, placing humankind and our functions and the associations between these functions in relationship to the environment.

Appendix Four

Meridian Relationships

This "mother-son law" explains a number of pathologic mechanisms. For example, when the mother is ill, a disequilibrium and thus an illness can be brought on in the son. Inversely, when the son is ill, a disease in the mother can be provoked. An example of this mother-son law is the relationship of the liver-heart. If the liver is diseased, the heart may become diseased as well. We observe this sequence in right heart insufficiency that is consequent to the hypertension of the hepatic veins in cirrhosis. Inversely, a cardiac insufficiency can lead to "cardiac liver." The *Ling Shou* states:

> Pains of the heart that are accompanied by a pale, cadaverous hue to the skin of the face are symptoms indicative of liver problems. It is necessary in this case to prick the second and third points of the liver meridian, *xing jian* and *tai chong*.

Beyond the luo and yuan points and numerous other points of lesser importance, there are five essential points on each meridian that are points of resonance for each of the five elements. These points are called *ting, rong, shu, jing,* and *he,* and comprise the five ancient *shu* points *(wu shu xue).* Wood corresponds to ting, fire to rong, earth to shu, metal to jing, water to he. For all the meridians, these five shu points are located between the hand and elbow for the upper limbs and between the foot and knee for the lower limbs. These zones are important because they are the portion of the meridians where the change of polarity operates when a yin meridian gives rise to a yang meridian, or vice versa. It is therefore at the terminal or proximal portion of a meridian that it is easiest to influence the polarity of a meridian, increasing or diminishing its polarity by appropriately influencing one of the five shu points.

As can be seen in the following illustration, the correspondence of these points is different for the yin and yang functions. In both cases the first point of the meridian, the most extreme point, corresponds to the period in which there occurs the transition from yin to yang. The ting point that is the first of the meridians of yin organs corresponds to spring, because it is the place where yin is changeable into yang. The ting point that is the first of the meridians of yang organs corresponds to autumn, because it is the place where yang is changeable into yin.

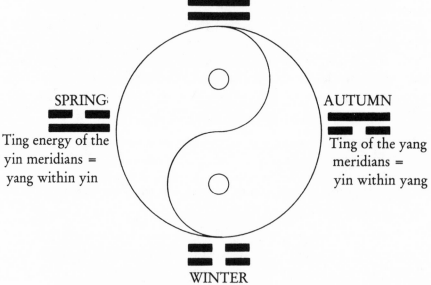

SUMMER
Rong energy of the yin meridians = heat = yang within yang

SPRING
Ting energy of the
yin meridians =
yang within yin

AUTUMN
Ting of the yang
meridians =
yin within yang

WINTER
Rong of the yang meridians = cold = yin within yin

Yin meridians   Yang meridians

Figure 20: The shu antique points

Antagonism exists between the polarities of the points. This is especially true of the rong point of yin meridians, which corresponds to heat, to total yang, in opposition to the rong point of yang meridians, which corresponds to cold, to total yin.

This view of the magnetic nature of the meridians is similar to that of the meridians of the magnetosphere of the earth, after which the body meridians were named:

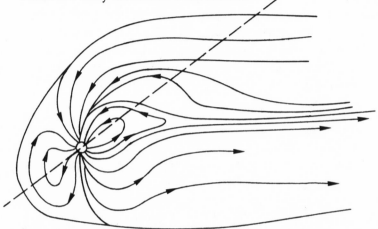

Figure 21: Meridian section of the magnetosphere (14)

The geomagnetic equator of man, at the level of the limbs, corresponds to the axis of the elbow for the arm and the axis of the knee for the leg. It is at this level that reversal can occur, before the most extreme point. The reversal occurs in five stages corresponding to the five polarized differentiations of the five elements, ting, rong, shu, jing, and he:

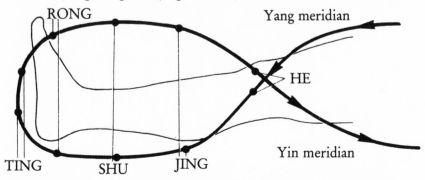

Figure 22: Reversal of yin-yang polarization in the lower limb

197

The five ancient shu points are used for reequilibration of the energy of the meridians. If an organ, for example the liver, retains too much energy and does not pass on its excess to the heart (the mother-son configuration), the acupuncturist will prick the fire point on the liver meridian, which will disperse the liver energy for the benefit of the heart. This point is *xing jiang* (LV-2). This is the point the early Chinese authors recommend in the treatment of cardiac trouble of hepatic origin. In the same manner, given the individual in whom the heart is found to have an insufficient energy, the acupuncturist may prick the wood (liver) point of the heart meridian, the tonification point for the heart. It is even possible to combine the two points with effective results.

Contemporary research of ancient shu points has revealed that it is possible to visually ascertain their action by a variety of techniques, including radiology, fluoroscopy, and manometric tests, as well as studies of secretory responses to specific stimuli directed to the various points. *(5,29)*

The law of domination and repression also is operative in the shu points. For example, if the kidney meridian is weak due to the domination of the spleen-pancreas meridian, it is possible to protect the kidney by pricking the earth (spleen) point of the kidney meridian. The acupuncturist can also slow down the activity of the pancreas by pricking the water (kidney) point of the spleen meridian. This principle holds for all the laws of correspondence in and among the elements. If the liver meridian is in repletion and the subject suffers from muscular contractions or nervousness due to excessive ingestion of acidic or bitter foods, the acupuncturist can use the point corresponding to the flavor that most corrects the excess, which is the mild or sweet flavor corresponding to the earth. The acupuncturist will prick the earth point of the liver meridian, *tai chong* (LV-3).

Appendix Five

Research and Experimental Models

The interest aroused in the West about the efficacy of acupuncture in surgical anesthesia has initiated experimentation in American and European hospitals and universities, as well as in Eastern countries. Such experimentation usually involves testing the clinical effects of acupuncture in one or another medical specialty on one or another syndrome.

The Western interest has in turn prompted renewed interest in the East, especially in China and Vietnam. A significant result of this interest was the First National Acupuncture Symposium on Moxibustion and Acupuncture Anesthesia, held in China in June, 1979. In the course of this congress the results of hundreds of clinical and physiologic studies were presented by research teams from the most important cities of China, including Canton, Shanghai, Nanking, Beijing. The experiments often involved patient and/or subject populations of several hundreds or thousands, and concerned periods of ten years or more. The specialties investigated were diverse, and included pathology, cardiology, gastroenterology, urology, gynecology, obstetrics, and psychiatry. Many of the reports were translated into English and published by the government of China. The principal points of this publication were also translated into French by Professor Bossy of the Montpellier faculty (5).

Much of the reasoning behind research in acupuncture is based on the hypothesis that acupuncture acts by stimulating specific cutaneous regions. The supposed areas are stimulated and the results are interpreted according to our present knowledge of physiology and its molecular basis.

199

This approach is potentially rich in its yield of information on the mechanisms of action of acupuncture. In the West, where research has been directed primarily to the mechanism of action of acupuncture anesthesia, the recent discovery of endorphins, internal secretions pharmacologically similar in action to morphine, has resulted in the hypothesis that the mechanism of anesthesia is due to the secretion of endorphins resulting from the cutaneous stimulation of the acupuncture points.

However, a biological basis is not the only one that can be used in the study of acupuncture. A second basis is an extension of the anatomic model that acupuncture postulates. As we have seen, the Western and Chinese views of anatomy are different. Western anatomy is organic and material; Chinese anatomy is energetic and non-material. One can explore experimentally the nature of the meridians, namely, the physical phenomena associated with them, especially at the level of the acupuncture points.

The obstacle to this path is that it requires the researchers, physicists in particular, to understand the nature of the polarized energy postulated by the Chinese. The predominant view that acupuncture is in the domain of medicine has prompted a greater interest in its research by clinicians than physicists. This is why, on the whole, such experimentation has been proportionally less common and advanced than that of clinical and physiological research (38).

A third approach, radically opposed at present, consists of trying to deepen our Western knowledge of physiology and medicine through a study of the body according to the Chinese concept of man. Unfortunately it is almost impossible, given the present scientific spirit in the West, to envisage such an approach. Due to the rationalistic principles that form the base of the bulk of Western science, development of anything like acupuncture would probably never have occurred, nor would investigations of the physical nature of bioelectric networks. Yet, demonstration of the efficacy of its techniques has already been shown in anesthesia, and its existence scientifically established in various fundamental and crucial experiments, including electrical and electromagnetic measurements, photo-thermographics, and photographic techniques in electromagnetic fields (already commercialized for acupuncturists).

The availability of such techniques should prompt further research and thus advance our knowledge and verification of the validity of acupuncture. The oneness concept of the mind and body that is so prevalent in Chinese medicine can then be used as a model that links the terrain, which is connected to the biologic functions and their genetic determinants, to the behavior that marks the character type and physiologic and psychologic reactions.

Endnotes

[1] *Editor's Note:* Dr. Requena is referring to European research. Acupuncture was acculturated in Europe earlier than in the United States. By the late 1950's scholars and physicians in France had access to translations of the Chinese sources, the experience of practitioners in the Orient, and a Vietnamese subculture living in France. All these sources contributed to an earlier advancement of acupuncture. Serious study of acupuncture in the United States generally begin in the late 1970's. As of the date of publication of this text, Japan and France are the leading sources of clinical research that meets Western standards. Basic research, however, is progressing rapidly here. The works of Robert Becker (such as *The Body Electric*) are a good example and very readable.

[2] Successive acupuncture treatments also have been shown to be beneficial for persons suffering from shingles. The pain diminishes as does the frequency and intensity of the outbreaks. The effect of the acupuncture treatment is consequently to curtail the normal course of the disease process. Thus, to confine the application of acupuncture to the alleviation of pain is to limit greatly the scope of its therapeutic potential. Acupuncture, with repeated application, alters mechanisms that are fundamental to disease processes. The alteration involves a reequilibration of the energy that circulates in the acupuncture meridians on which are located the specific acupuncture points.

[3] The mechanism or action is the same as the action that corrects an organic disruption. The insomniac will not necessarily sleep soundly on the night of the initial acupuncture session, but, after several sessions, generally four or five, he or she notices that sleep occurs more rapidly. There is also less agitation during the night, awakening does not occur too early, and the sleep is more restorative. If the therapist continues treatment at regular intervals, the

sleep function is progressively reequilibrated. The person returns to patterns typical of those prior to the onset of insomnia. Thus, acupuncture does not act merely as a sleeping tablet, immediately and only symptomatically, but acts on the basic physiology of the body, gradually effecting a reestablishment of a functional equilibrium.

[4] Many studies have occurred since the original French language publication of this text. In addition to tobacco, narcotic withdrawal and detoxification have been treated. Results have continued to be favorable, and New York's Lincoln Hospital acupuncture detoxification program under the direction of Dr. Michael Smith has become a national model in the United States.

The results of a study on the effects of acupuncture on tobacco detoxification illustrate the efficacy of acupuncture treatment on drug dependence. In a group of 500 persons enrolled in a detoxification program administered by a hospital in 1975 and 1976, one-half of the smokers were given acupuncture treatment in which the needles were inserted at exactly the prescribed points, and the other half received needles inserted just adjacent to the prescribed points. All subjects were given the same explanations of the treatment. The following week the subjects were examined. Among those in whom the needles were inserted adjacent to the prescribed points, 17% were successful in not smoking; among those in which the needles were inserted appropriately, 85% were successful in discontinuing smoking. Seventeen percent is not even the usual level ascribed to the placebo effect, an effect presumed to be due to autosuggestion and usually cited as 30%. After the initial interview the subjects who had received needle insertion adjacent to the prescribed points were treated by needles inserted into the appropriate insertion points, including the 17% who had stopped smoking but who felt nonetheless an imperative need for it. Once again, 85% of the subjects stopped smoking.

The example illustrates not only the efficacy of acupuncture in the treatment of psychological problems, it also illustrates the need for correct needle insertion. Should the acupuncturist make a mistake in choosing the appropriate acupuncture points, the action is less effective, slower, or even absent. Yet, from the moment that the mistake is corrected, even without informing the patient of the

change, a noticeable improvement is felt by the patient. Th[...]
improvement usually is revealed in the next acupuncture session.

Editor's Note: Smoking cessation studies in the United States have
been less dramatic. It is difficult to say whether this indicates poor
acupuncture, less rigidly controlled studies, different populations,
or different evaluations. Those seeking this help should speak
with their physician and/or an acupuncturist.

[5] *Editor's Note:* Interested readers may wish to refer to *Hara Diagnosis* for current research in the biomagnetic aspects of the meridial systems.

[6] To extend the analogy further, let us consider constipation by
way of example. Analysis of the patient and the symptoms permits the acupuncturist to determine whether the constipation is a
spasmodic constipation, from excess contraction of the large intestine, or atonic constipation, from insufficient contraction, which
is usually the case in older people. If the acupuncturist determines
the constipation is a spasmodic constipation and chooses to treat
the patient via the large intestine meridian (which is not necessarily the appropriate meridian), the energy of the large intestine
must be dispersed through a point on this meridian that is
involved in this function. For the large intestine meridian this is
the second point, which is located on the index finger. If, on the
contrary, the constipation is an atonic constipation, the eleventh
point, which is located in the fold of the elbow, must be pricked
(and sometimes heated).

But, as has been mentioned, treatment is not limited solely to
points on the large intestine meridian. One could, especially in
the case of spasms of the colon, prick *neiguan* (PC-6), the "internal
barrier," and also search for certain acupuncture points on the
abdomen that are painful to touch. These latter points are those
on the skin where the constipation and spasm in the intestine are
projected. The point(s) could be on the stomach meridian, on the
spleen meridian, on the kidney meridian or ren mai, etc. These
points of projection become reflex zones, and therapeutic action
on them must not be neglected. The phenomenon has been seen
by Western neurophysiologists who have named them reflex der-
matalgias. These acupuncture points have been found to

assic, diagnostic reflex zones defined by Western
as the MacBurney point of appendicitis
:o the 26th point of the stomach meridian), and
:osto-vertebral angle in patients with nephritic col-
ing exactly to *jingmen* (GB-25), a point for treat-
; suffering from renal disease.

[7] Let us suppose that a subject is suffering from excess energy of
the gallbladder meridian. This excess can be manifested by anger,
digestive troubles, repeated migraine attacks, buzzing in the ears,
ocular spasms, insomnia, or tachycardia. The propitious hour for
dispersing the energy of this meridian would be from 11 p.m. to 1
a.m. If, on the other hand, the subject is suffering from insufficient energy of the gallbladder meridian, and the meridian thus
needs to be tonified or energized, it should be done in the following hour, from 1 a.m. to 3 a.m. This method is described in the
ancient texts as meeting and then pursuing the meridian.

However, from a practical standpoint, the acupuncturist's office is
closed at this hour. Furthermore, it is the hour that the late
sleeper seeks sleep and is on the verge of attaining it. For these
and other reasons an alternative route must be taken, and the
theories of acupuncture provide for such an alternative. It is possible to prick the point of the meridian at the opposite hour, from
11 a.m. to 1 p.m., the hour of the heart meridian. If one tonifies
the heart at this time it is equivalent to dispersing the energy of
the gallbladder. We see then that the circadian rhythm has an
interesting, opposite relationship among the meridians, which is
called the midnight-noon relationship.

[8] Jing circulates in the eight particular meridians (extra channels)
and the 12 secondary and particular meridians linked to the 12
principal meridians. This energy is distinct from the nourishing
energy called rong that circulates in the arteries and principal
meridians. These secondary and particular (distinct) meridians all
have a centripetal course. They begin in an arm or leg, extend to a
corresponding organ, and pass to the heart. From there they continue up to the brain. Thus, the jing elaborated in the meridian
will take the path of either the eight particular meridians or its distinct meridian. By the latter route the jing is conducted to the
heart. The heart plays a significant role here, for from it is

elaborated a specific, essential energy through the CNS that travels to the brain via the distinct meridian.

[9] See further, Appendix One, "Heart — Brain Duality."

[10] See Appendix Two, "Cybernetic Organization in Biology."

[11] Complementarity and the transformation of excess into its opposite are illustrated by biological feedback mechanisms. For example, the pituitary gland secretes ACTH, a hormone that stimulates the adrenal gland to secrete cortisol. When the level of cortisol is elevated in the blood it inhibits the activity of the pituitary gland, which then ceases to secrete ACTH.

The principle of antagonism also operates in nerve impulse conduction, by the exchange of sodium and potassium across the membrane. It also occurs in the regulation of blood pressure, of oxygen and carbon dioxide pressures in the blood, in the elimination of salt by the kidney, in the regulation of blood glucose — in short, in all biological metabolism.

[12] Interested practitioners are directed to the more detailed work, *Terrains and Pathology in Acupuncture.*

[13] See: Appendix Three, "Classification."

[14] See: Appendix Four, "Meridian Relationships."

[15] This relationship is said to be the basis, for example, of anemias or diseases of the spleen that are accompanied by anorexia (loss of appetite). The latter symptom is more understandable in view of the relationship between the digestive activity of the stomach and its hematologic activity in the absorption of vitamin B12, and the functions of the spleen.

[16] See further, Appendix Four, "Meridian Relationships."

[17] *Editor's Note:* These medicines are not currently available in the United States. They are produced by European pharmaceutical companies as both oral and injectable liquids, and available there through physicians who practice the diathetic system.

Western medical practice in the United States is marked by a greater exclusivity than in Europe. Thus, the herbal (phytotherapy) medicine and trace element preparations (diathetic medicine) have found no sponsor for the expensive and lengthy F.D.A. protocol process. While these medicines are not chemical drugs, any substance labeled with an indication or symptom recognized by medicine must acquire F.D.A. approval before it can be sold. Currently, work done for overseas approvals is not accepted in the U.S. Diathetic medicines are an extremely small concentration of the trace element, far smaller than drug doses, but larger than homeopathic dilutions.

[18] An illustration of this might be, for example, a Yang Ming-metal and Jue Yin girl, nervous and phlegmatic. Her father is Yang Ming-metal and Tai Yang, a phlegmatic passionate type, but she has received from him only his coolness. Morphologically she gets from him a certain thinness of the face, a rather long and fine nose, and a slightly curved back. Pathologically the vulnerability of the Yang Ming meridian and the metal constitution makes her suffer from slight constipation, frequent colds beginning in autumn, and multiple dental caries.

Her mother, Jue Yin and Shao Yang, is pure wood. She is hyperemotive, myopic, and has suffered all her life from migraines, painful menstruation, and varicose veins. She was operated on for fibroma. She has strong allergies in spring, with sneezing. The girl has her mother's large, expressive eyes. She also gets from her mother a great nervousness. She blushes easily, is in anguish more than the average person over small things. But beyond the anxiety there is also a certain control that comes from her father. She reasons with herself and is never totally troubled, and thus never becomes quite panic-stricken like her mother. Likewise she does not have the life-of-the-party personality nor the angry side of her mother. She is more passive, although irritable. From the wood constitution of the mother she has neither migraines nor myopia; on the contrary she is far-sighted like her father. She does not suffer during her menstruation; at most she is merely more irritable. By contrast, she suffers from vein problem, varices, and hemorrhoids.

She is surprised by her absurd fits of anxiety that she cannot explain and tries to dispel. She would not admit to herself the enormous stage fright she had at the time of taking her drivers' text. It is the phlegmatic side that reacts; by contrast, her frivolous side makes her reproach her lack of spontaneity at times and her incapacity to respond positively to the unexpected. It is the nervous side that rebels. There is in her also a certain hard authority and gruffness for which she reproaches herself in her dealings with her own children. She recognizes she was herself subject to the same gruffness and authority from her own father when she was a child. It is the imperceptible Tai Yang, the passionate aspect that she inherited from him, but which in her comes through only slightly, and which, except physically, has made no significant impact on her either in her early years or presently. In her CE-40, the Tai Yang would be the type with the third or fourth highest score.

[19] An ancient text of Chinese chiromancy (palmistry), translated by George Soulie de Morant, defines five types of hands as a function of the planets (36). These planets correspond to the five elements. This work forms the basis for our description of the hands and their association with five different body constitutions.

[20] Using oligotherapy, for example, the trace elements zinc, nickel, and cobalt might be dispensed to re-equilibrate the glycemic cycle of the pancreas; or copper, gold, and silver could reinforce the defenses of the organism and diminish or totally stop pharyngeal infections during childhood, often preventing removal of the tonsils.

[21] Even renal malformation can be predicted by an analysis of the temperament of the individual. If the child is of Shao Yin temperament — sentimental, susceptible to cold, suffering from pharyngeal inflammations (sore throat) or otitis (earache), even in the absence of urinary signs, like lumbar pain — the possibility of renal malformation should be considered.

[22] *Editor's Note:* The "Berger test" is the French language survey developed by Berger; the problems concerning that test, as detailed by the statistics in this section, lead to Gex's adaptation and improvement, the "Characterologic Evaluation — 40." The "CE-40" is the author's English-language adaptation of the test by

Gex and is the one used in chapter 5. The statistical measures used in the text preceding this chapter refer to CE-40 studies. The "Minnesota multiphasic" is the same MMPI with which the American psychologist will be familiar.

[23] A more detailed discussion of these themes, reviewing hysteria, anguish, schizophrenia, perversion, and melancholy, may be found in *Terrains & Pathology in Acupuncture*.

[24] The Chinese speak of fire here because the subject is metal. Metal fears fire because, in the symbolism of the five elements, fire melts metal. This example illustrates again the Chinese inclination to view psychological disequilibria as originating by energetic mechanisms.

[25] In our statistical study of the 133 subjects already mentioned, we demonstrated a significant correlation between the character type and the associated symptoms of the individuals. Nervous subjects showed greater frequency of several symptoms predicted by acupuncture : allergy, varices, migraines, spasms, etc.

[26] The specificity of the symptoms dictated by the diatheses and temperaments aids in the verification of the clinical signs suggested by the findings in the pulses, which are in practice rather subjective. The pulses too are subject to variations, such as those subsequent to meals, cigarette smoking, coffee, and medications.

[27] The redox (oxidation-reduction) potential is linked to pH and rH2 by the equation $rH2 = 2pH + 33.33E$.

Bibliography

1. Alexander, F. *La Medecine psycho-somatique, ses principes et ses applications.* Paris: E. Payot, 1962.

2. Bejart, M. *Un instant dans la vie d'autrui.* Paris: Ed. Flammarion, 1979.

3. Berger, G. *Traite pratique d'analyse du caractere.* Paris: Presses Universitaires de France, 1972.

4. Bossy, J. 1978. "Les rhythmes dans la medecine chinoise et leurs correspondances en Occident." *Revue Meridiens* 43-44:67-105.

5. Bossy, J. *Synthese des travaux des Symposia d'acupuncture de Pekin 1979.* Doin, 1980.

6. Brient-Clabaux, M.J. 1980. "Le systeme 'Redox' est la cle de voute de l'harmonie biologique." *Le Quot.du Med.* 2264:11 Sept.

7. Brosse, T. *La "Conscience-energie," structure de l'homme et de l'univers.* Sisteron: Ed. Presence, 1978.

8. Capra, F. *Le Tao de la physique.* Paris: Ed. Tchou, 1975.

9. Chamfrault, A. *Huang Di Nei Jing Su Wen (Traite de Medecine chinoise)* tome II. Angouleme: Ed. Coquemard, 1959.

10. Charon, J.E. *L'esprit, cet inconnu.* Paris: Ed. Albin Michel, 1977.

11. Corman, L. *Nouveau manuel de morpho-psychologie.* Paris: Ed. Stock-plus, 1966, 1977.

12. Debaux, J.O. *Essai sur la pharmacie et la matiere medecale des Chinois.* Paris, 1865.

13. Delay, J. *Introduction a la medecine psycho-somatique.* Paris: Ed. Masson, 1961.

14. Encyclopedia Universalis. "Typologies psychologiques" 13:767-770. Paris: Ed. Encycl. Universalis, S.A., 1975.

15. Freud, S. *Inhibition, symptomes et angoisse.* Paris: P.U.F., 1968.

17. Granet, M. *La pensee chinoise.* Paris: Ed. Albin Michel, 1968.

18. Grimaldi-Pain, G. 1981. "Comportements et predispositions morbides en acupuncture et medecine fonctionnelle." Marseille. Medical doctoral thesis.

19. Groddeck, G. *Ca et moi.* Paris: N.R.F., 1977.

20. Husson, A. *Huang Di Nei Jing Su Wen.* Paris: Ed. A.S.M.A.F., 1973.

21. Laborit, H. *L'agressivite detournee.* Collec. 10/18. Paris: Union Generale d'Edition, 1970.

22. ———. *La nouvelle grille.* Collec. Liberte 1000. Paris: Ed. Robert Laffont, 1974.

23. Lavier, J. *Histoire, doctrine et pratique de l'acupuncture chinoise.* Paris: Ed. Henri Veyrier, 1974.

24. Linquette, M. *Precis d'endocrinologie.* Paris: Ed. Masson, 1979.

25. MacLean, M.D. 1966. "Brain and vision in the evolution of emotional and sexual behavior." New York. Thomas William Salmon Lecture, Academy of Medicine.

26. Maspero, H. *Le Taoisme et les religions chinoises.* Paris: Ed. Gallimard, 1971.

27. Menetrier, J. *La medecine des fonctions.* Paris: Ed. Le Francois, 1974.

28. ———. *Introduction a une psycholophysiologie experimentale.* Paris: Ed. Le Francois, 1967.

29. Mussat, M. *Physique de l'acupuncture. Hypotheses et approches experimentales.* Paris: Ed. Le Francois, 1974.

30. Nguyen van Nghi. *Pathogenie et pathologie energetiques en medecine chinoise.* Marseille: Imp. Don Bosco, 1971.

31. Needham, J. *La science chinoise et l'Occident*. Paris: Ed. du Seuil, 1973.

32. ———. *Science and civilisation in China. Chemistry and Chemical Technology*. Cambridge, England: Cambridge University Press, 1974.

33. Requena, Y. *Terrains and Pathology in Acupuncture* 1. Brookline: Paradigm Publications, 1986.

34. ———. *Terrains et Pathologie en Acupuncture* 2. Paris: Librarie Maloine, 1982.

35. Salducci, E., and S. Heller. 1979. "Vous avez dit psychosomatique?" Thesis for masters degree in psychotherapy. University of Aix'Marseille.

36. Soulie de Morant, G. *Traite de chiromancie chinoise*. Paris: Ed. Guy Tredaniel, 1978.

37. Watson, L. *Histoire naturelle du surnaturel*. Paris: Ed. Albin Michel, 1974.

38. Wolpe, P.R. 1985. "The Maintenance of Professional Authority: Acupuncture and the American Physician." *Social Problems* 32:5.

Water going the wrong way.   Dec 5
                              199.
Instead of feeding wood - putting out the fire
stiff muscles - dryness
K. Yin deficiency? Hormonal Imbalance
• Anger Frustrate Irritable Sadness Anxiety
Fear Loss of joy.
• Energy blocked - Cannot flow -
Destruction ko Gabi,
• Had to move away from Trees Tgo Thyro
Gall bladder - Zig Zag hormonal
void